THE
RESILIENCY
QUEST

MORE PRAISE FOR THE RESILIENCY QUEST

"A physician's life is typically busy, rushed and can be overwhelming. Doug McKinley teaches us how to organize our career in a way that will maximize meaning, satisfaction and resiliency. Physician burnout is more common than ever, however with Doug as your "trail guide" you will find purpose and resiliency. This book is a must read for physicians at any point in their career!"

Hugh S. Taylor, MD
Professor and Chair
Obstetrics and Gynecology
Yale School of Medicine

"A clear and insightful book for physician leaders. Filled with practical information, great advice, facts, and personal anecdotes. Highly recommended as the one book they should all read."

JoNell Efantis Potter, PhD, APRN, FAAN
Professor and Vice Chair for Research
Department of Obstetrics, Gynecology and Reproductive Sciences
University of Miami Miller School of Medicine, Miami, Florida

---

"Doug's book is a tool that imparts tangible, pragmatic life lessons that can be used the minute a page is turned or a chapter is closed. It has the potential to lighten a load and provide introspection, support and guidance. It is hope. And that is the best gift to our physicians."

Lisa Laurent, MD MBA MS CPE FAAPL
Chief Medical Officer
CHI St. Alexius Health & Physician Enterprise
Bismarck, North Dakota

"This book by Doug McKinley is a continuation of his personal journey to assist all healthcare leaders to understand how to adapt to the ever-changing world of today's healthcare industry. His writing style is matter of fact and engages the read. Using the principles of psychology applied to cognitive adaptation, he provides guidance for healthcare leaders in various phases of their career. This book will assist all physicians with modifying their interpretation of the new world order and becoming resilient to altering your core values and thus, reducing your risk for development of burnout."

Fred A. Luchette, MD, MSc
Vice Chair, VA Affairs
Professor of Surgery
Loyola University of Chicago
Chief of Surgical Services, Hines VA
Department of Surgery

"Doug McKinley is an accomplished expert at helping physicians regain their emotional and professional traction in times of uncertainty and crisis. Some of us want to throw up our arms and give up in the midst of the current emergency of physician burnout. Dr. McKinley gives clinicians the tools to take things into their own hands, based on real-world experience and in a manner that imitates the relationship-building he does with clients. Adverse circumstances do not have to define us in a harmful way; we can create great strength from them, and this is one of the tools in the toolkit to do this."

Christian Pettker, MD
Professor of Obstetrics, Gynecology & Reproductive Sciences
Yale School of Medicine

"Relatable, vulnerable, and engaging through a first-person narrative, this is a book that burns the burnout in physicians. A solution rather than label. A book that puts you in a quest towards resilience and understanding of self and others so as to adapt to our ever-changing world as we are led and lead others to success as physician leaders in both clinical and administrative careers."

James Paul C Maganito, DO, MPH, MHA, CHES, CIS, FACOOG
Chief of Staff, MT VA Healthcare System
Obstetrician and Gynecologist
Department of Surgery
Fort Harrison, Montana

"A quick-access list of lessons to keep us focused on what matters most in our journeys as leaders and change agents in healthcare."

Aldo Peixoto, MD
Professor and Vice Chair for Quality & Safety
Department of Internal Medicine
Yale School of Medicine

Directed towards health care providers, this book is filled with practical and meaningful suggestions to face the complex challenge of achieving and sustaining meaningful resilience. Doug's unique and extensive experience is distilled into this relatable and conversational work that should give confidence to the reader that achieving a goal of a stronger resiliency muscle is not only achievable, but truly an enjoyable lifelong quest.

David W. Hecht, MD, MS, MBA
Executive Vice President for Clinical Affairs and Regional CMO
(retired)
Loyola University Health System

"Doug McKinley's book is an important piece of work at a critically important time for physicians. Having worked closely with world class physicians for 30 years, it is clear the pressures of today's healthcare environment are at an all-time high for doctors. They are continually asked to do more with less, and too often they prioritize their own mental, emotional and physical health last. Doug's book is a thoughtful, engaging, and encouraging read for physicians who want to reenergize their life's work and build their resilience to the pressures of today's clinical environment."

Jeff Hutchison
Vice President of Commercial Operations, Motus GI Holdings

"Where was this book when I needed it most?! This long overdue book is a must read for all physicians. I challenge healthcare organizations to incorporate it into their processes for appointment and reappointment, leadership development and health and wellness."

Inginia Genao, MD
Diversity, Equity and Inclusion Leader
Yale School of Medicine

"Throughout my career as a healthcare consultant, I have seen many physicians struggle personally due to work demands and even more when placed in leadership positions. In this book, Doug provides the reader valuable tools and a success formula for those who have a desire to make a difference (or even just show up for work) yet feel overwhelmed and exhausted. A must-read leadership book that ignites the passion of physician or any healthcare provider."

Daniel J. Marino
Managing Partner
Lumina Health Partners

ACKNOWLEDGMENTS

My first and last acknowledgment has to be my wife, Jana. She genuinely believes in me and supports me in my life's work to invest in leaders and their personal journeys to become better human beings. Jana, thank you for tirelessly tracking every word of this book while serving as my primary developmental editor. Your tenacity to make my message clearer and more succinct is remarkable and I will be forever grateful.

I would also like to acknowledge Dr. Lynn Tanoue whose vision to put simple and practical suggestions into the hands of physicians brought this book to life. Lynn, your encouragement and belief in me and our work with RISE at Yale inspired me to share this information in written form and I am very grateful that you "see me."

Many physicians and healthcare leaders (too many to list) volunteered to read the first draft and offer their input. While it was a bit nerve wracking to put my work out there in that initial state, your specific and thoughtful feedback was critical in shaping the final version. You made the long hours of deliberating over phrases and stories worthwhile. Thank you for your generous feedback. It was incredibly affirming.

Other contributors to the refining of this book include Lucy Zielinski, a friend and healthcare colleague, who generously offered her editing expertise. Deb Rickert, a friend and founder of Leap of Faith, an experiential based transformational program, brought the story of Louise alive in the closing chapter titled Collateral Beauty. Thank you both for sharing your time and talent for this project.

Louise Cantrell, thanks for sharing your personal story with us. Having faced your darkest realities with grit and courage, you are a beautiful example of what resiliency can look like. You have modeled the authentic journey of dancing with both sadness and hope.

Adam Mock, your talent and creativity will always be an inspiration to me. I am grateful you accepted my invitation to help with the cover and trailhead designs and my podcast mark. I loved your investment to read the whole book before putting pencil to paper in creating the artistic expression of this journey toward resiliency.

I also want to thank lifelong friends Jeff and Robbin Grigsby for your support and sharing your beautiful Michigan lake house with me. The ability to get away and be alone to think and write was so meaningful and helpful. Having an amazing setting to both engage my imagination and keep my focus was essential to completing this book.

I am very grateful to be considered a personal coach and confidant to so many amazing physician leaders around the country. Watching all of you work so hard to serve and to advance better healing practices for your patients is incredible. I am indebted to all of you for being vulnerable with me and permitting me the honor to witness your work and participate in your leadership development.

Lastly, I want to again thank my wife Jana for her investment in me and my work. Many thanks as well to my adult children, Seth and Megan. You two have taught me so much about life and resiliency. I will forever be grateful for your love and support.

DOUG MCKINLEY PSY. D.

THE
RESILIENCY
QUEST

A JOURNEY OF PERSONAL LEADERSHIP DEVELOPMENT
FOR THE THRIVING PHYSICIAN

Dedicated to all the healthcare providers who give so much of yourselves to others.

May you continue to thrive on your resiliency journey.

The Resiliency Quest: *A Journey of Personal Leadership Development for the Thriving Physician*
Copyright © 2021 by Doug McKinley
Illustrations copyright © 2021 by Adam Mock

Doug McKinley Psy. D.
DLMPathways
www.dlmpathways.com

ISBN 978-1-7375725-2-7
Ebook ISBN 978-1-7375725-1-0

Cover design by Adam Mock
www.adammock.com

CONTENTS

FORWARD

A decade ago, our Department of Internal Medicine began an extensive restructuring of our onboarding process for new faculty, focusing on workshops that reflect our mission, values, and culture rather than granular operational details. This effort predated the tidal wave of appreciation of physician burnout and was serendipitously prescient as Internal Medicine is consistently among those specialties with the highest burnout levels. The evolution of our onboarding process reflects our strong desire to acknowledge the importance of life skills that build resilience, which we know is necessary to sustain a personally and professionally satisfying career in medicine.

Doug McKinley has been our mentor and strong partner in this onboarding initiative that we named RISE (Resiliency, Innovation, and Sustainable Excellence) at Yale. Doug is himself a clinician and deeply interested in understanding how physicians think, function, and behave. We engaged Doug to guide us in the development of our onboarding workshops, focusing on several of the key areas he discusses in this book, including resilience, self-awareness, and boundaries. Doug created a training course for the core faculty who facilitate the RISE at Yale workshops, which have continued to evolve over the several years since they were introduced. The feedback on the workshops from both facilitators and new faculty has been overwhelmingly positive.

In working together, Doug and I have had many conversations

about thriving, the antithesis to burnout. What is it that enables physicians, or anyone, to thrive? The answers to that vital question are complex and individual, but there are basic tenets that thriving physicians share and actually live. Doug identifies 5 principles as the underpinnings of thriving: Purpose, Awareness, Connection, Boundaries, and Agility. These are not theories; they are life skills. In one of our discussions, I suggested to Doug that he write a primer articulating these, a resource that would serve as a quick reference tool for our faculty after the workshops. I am thrilled that he has moved forward with that idea, framed now as The Resiliency Quest, and am optimistic that the positive and practical benefits of our workshops can be similarly experienced by other physicians who engage with the principles articulated in this book.

Lynn Tanoue, MD, MBA
Professor of Medicine
Vice Chair for Clinical Affairs, Department of Internal Medicine
Yale School of Medicine
New Haven, CT

INTRODUCTION

I have worked in the healthcare industry for over 30 years, both as a clinical psychologist with my own practice, and then later as a leadership development consultant to healthcare leaders. I've thoroughly enjoyed assisting and learning from individuals in both arenas.

For the last 20 years, I have focused my time on work with physicians like you. While we address and resolve various issues and challenges, I recognize one of the best ways I can serve you is to encourage you on your quest for resiliency.

What is resiliency? Why do you want to achieve it? How do you know when you are successful at or fall short of being resilient? I answer these questions in the following pages while dividing the rest of the book into sections that highlight resiliency learning in five areas:

1. Living from purpose
2. Learning from being more aware
3. Having a positive connection with others
4. Exemplifying healthy personal boundaries
5. Being agile enough to embrace needed change

At the end of each section are practical steps to follow and evidenced-based protocols to guide you on your resiliency quest.

No one is exempt from the twists and turns of life's unwanted demands. Like all professionals, you cannot buffer yourself from adversity despite all your talents, capabilities, and resources. Therefore, it is vitally important that you learn how to be resilient — to be masterful at facing and adapting emotionally to the highs, lows, and everything in between on your life's journey. That's why I chose to write this book. I want to help physicians learn ways to be resilient in both their careers and personal lives.

Each of you will face burnout and approach resiliency differently depending upon where you are in your career. If applied accordingly, the lessons in this book will benefit physicians in all three of the following seasons.

OUT OF THE GATE

You may be early in your career and these insights can provide you with an onboarding toolkit. I hope you use them as a way to find a healthy path forward as you face the questions and challenges of your next level milestones. Whether you end up finding your joy in research, clinical, or educational settings (or all three!), these lessons can be a companion guide. On every step along the journey, consider learning more about yourself, how you grow and take risks, and how to improve your workplace relationships. These growth areas and more are addressed and described specifically for you.

SPEEDING UP

You are likely in the midst of making pivotal changes in your career and/or deepening the commitment you started. I believe you may find some of these topics relevant to your current situation. The reality is that if you don't lift your head and hit pause once in a while, you may miss what is going on around you. These lessons can provide the sort of breathing space you've needed to situate yourself. Use this time as a way to reflect and nourish yourself. You are more than likely doing amazing things so make sure you are *being* as much as *doing*. In other words, I encourage you to be like a hiker on a journey, one who is focused on the trail you are on more than the destination you hope to reach. I will further expound on this important paradigm shift.

HITTING YOUR STRIDE

Hopefully you are at a wonderful place in your career. You may still be very busy yet realize the 'hunt' is slowing down. Maybe you're looking to invest in your profession differently and give back in other ways. There is always room to grow and learn. The lessons in this book can help reinforce concepts you've learned along the way. Or perhaps they can help you find better ways to mentor and assist your peers. I strongly encourage you to use this season of your career to invest in others.

Writing this book was inspired by the faithful physician leaders that I have been fortunate enough to spend quality time with. When I refer to physician leaders, I am talking about all physicians. My perspective is that leadership is not optional. I view leadership as necessary at all levels of an organization. Thus, physician leaders include you and your peers regardless of the roles and titles you may or may not have. The following pages include lessons I have learned from personal experience, from mentors and clients, and from subject matter experts in the leadership development field. I am confident these lessons will provide you with useful methods to become a more emotionally resilient, wildly effective, and vibrantly thriving physician. Now let's get started on your resiliency journey!

THE RESILIENCY QUEST

"What is it we are questing for? It is the fulfillment of that which is potential in each of us. Questing for it is not an ego trip; it is an adventure to bring into fulfillment your gift to the world, which is yourself."

~ *Joseph Campbell*

To begin, I want to share my thoughts and observations about the quest for resiliency by answering three questions I am often asked by you and your colleagues. I am hopeful my responses will compel you to invest time in reading the remainder of this book.

WHAT IS RESILIENCY?

You are often met, sometimes on a daily basis, with challenging situations, difficult choices, or uncooperative people that test your ability to respond appropriately and move forward. It is not always easy to be resilient in these circumstances. What is resiliency anyway? The American Psychological Association defines resilience as "the process of adapting well in the face of adversity, trauma, tragedy, threats, or significant sources of stress — such as family and relationship problems, serious health problems, or workplace and financial stressors. As much as resilience involves "bouncing back" from these difficult experiences, it can also involve profound personal growth."

I chose to use that definition because it encompasses two distinct facets of resiliency. First, it reflects the common understanding of resilience which is 'adapting well.' Second, it captures the thriving aspect of being resilient in the expression, 'profound personal growth.' I think of resiliency as both an adaptive and growth process. This has been true in my career and personal life when sources of stress often yielded the needed perspective that led me to adapt, learn, and grow. In my younger days, as a child of divorce I overcame that adversity by engaging in outside activities like sports and student body government. This gave me the support that I needed at that time. One of the more notable stressful experiences I recall, happened twenty years ago after I made the exciting decision to shift my career from being a clinician to becoming an organizational and leadership consultant. Unexpectedly, I was criticized by my professional peers and rejected by some who didn't understand my conviction to make this choice, which to them felt like a betrayal of my career as a clinician. There were many days when I wondered if I would buckle under the scrutiny of others and the pressure from entering a new field. But I pushed through believing that this was the right decision for me and my family. In doing so, I began healing from my need to please, found a deeper meaning in my career, and essentially lived from purpose rather than circumstance. While several of my colleagues were frustrated with me and confused by my desire to leave my practice and pursue something different, I resolutely endeavored to build a new career identity. Similarly, I witness how you encounter ongoing stressful and tricky circumstances as physicians and am encouraged by the resilience that some of you possess to see you through. As an example, you may choose to accept an administrative role or pursue national leadership responsibilities while understanding you may risk losing credibility from those who believe clinicians should solely be clinicians. There are some physicians though, who have a harder time navigating stressful circumstances and could benefit from learning ways to be more adaptive when things don't go as planned or there is an affinity toward trying something new. Whether you push through or struggle with adversity the following lessons in this book can assist you with that learning.

One thing I want you to realize is that a physician's resiliency quest is a *lifelong intentional pursuit*. The intention is to be physically, mentally, socially and emotionally healthy while also achieving professional satisfaction. I believe resiliency is the result of making a series of forward focused choices instead of it simply happening to you. Most people can survive a set-back, but only those who are truly intentional and thus thrive, turn 'lemons into lemonade' or 'failure into opportunity.' Surviving and thriving are very different. Surviving leaves you feeling relieved whereas thriving leads to inspiration and a new found strength. Instead of surviving your career, I truly hope you engage the quest to be resilient and thrive in it. It takes intentionality, effort, and skill to persevere and sometimes change course when the going gets tough. If you want to be a thriving physician, then resiliency needs to be intentionally pursued. Most often the pursuit is a challenging, uncomfortable, and sometimes unclear journey, but I do believe it is a necessary and worthy one to take. Overall, I believe resiliency is an intentional choice to be on a journey that involves adapting to, learning from, and growing in the challenging circumstances that intersect your life.

WHY QUEST FOR RESILIENCY?

To quest for something means to pursue or chase after it. To be on mission. To quest for resiliency means you choose to seek ways to push through the hard stuff. You are deliberate in moving forward even when it's difficult or doesn't make sense at the time. Obviously, questing to be resilient is not a one and done deal. It is an ongoing pursuit of acquiring and refining the skills necessary to bend and adapt to your personal and professional challenges. To be sure, those challenges will come and may get more intense as your career unfolds. Therefore, it will serve you well and set you up for meaningful success if you determine to learn ways to be a resilient physician.

With the ongoing changes in healthcare and the fast pace at which some of those changes are happening, questing for resiliency helps prepare you to navigate those changes, both big and small. Some of these transitions are causing extreme stress and burnout among physicians. Let me say that I don't believe you are responsible for the accelerated pace of change and the rapidly shifting and increasing demands on your time. So much of what happens is out of your control, such as the transition to electronic medical records, the shift to value based care, and of course this current global pandemic. It is all the more reason to quest for resiliency. To build those resilient muscles that will keep you strong when unforeseen changes cross your path.

When I was in high school, it was all about sports and fitting in with my peers. Instead of going to school to learn, I was trying to get noticed and belong. Not until late in my junior year did it occur to me that there may be some value in learning. So, I chose to focus on my classes and then head to college and graduate school. I still became distracted at times and felt under pressure to just finish school thereby forgetting why I was there in the first place which was to learn and grow. There are many times in my life that I wish I could go back and engage differently, not because I have regret, but because I could have learned so much more. And isn't that what life is all about? Living and learning to the fullest? Questing for resiliency certainly helps in that endeavor.

HOW DO YOU KNOW IF YOU ARE RESILIENT?

You know you are resilient by the way in which you *lead* your life. I emphasize lead because so many people give their power away to others and unforeseen external circumstances, both of which are out of their control. Resilient people on the other hand, live from the inside out relying on their own convictions to guide them while learning from and adapting to work and life challenges. They maintain a choice in their journey. Are you at full choice in your journey as a physician, able to flex and change course if needed? Or are you focused solely on achieving status or monetary goals? Or trying to attend to challenges that are out of your control, believing that if you could only conquer them, you would be fulfilled? If so, I invite you to think of your journey as taking a long hike. As in life, hiking is often more about the experiences you have along the way than about reaching a specific landing place (that is if you are open to a different view of success). Being fully aware of what you want and why you want it can be discovered by being truly honest with yourself about your motivations. For example, I am no longer convinced that the summits, or accomplishments in life will be any more fulfilling than the hike, or journey itself. Perhaps we need to rethink our preoccupation with conquering our challenges and replace that with the joy of hiking through them. Resiliency is mastering a way of life rather than accomplishing a specific goal. Again, it is being willing to learn ways of becoming and remaining adaptive and flexible. I imagine that you want not only to be successful in your career but also to be resiliently healthy and fulfilled by that experience.

I have listed some behaviors in the graph on the following page to help you get a quick overview of what it looks like to either have resiliency or lack resiliency in the five learning areas I mentioned in the introduction.

HAVE OR LACK RESILIENCY?

	HAVE RESILIENCY	LACK RESILIENCY
PURPOSE	Your success is in how well you serve others.	Your success only matters to you.
	You believe all people want to be their best.	You are chronically disappointed by others.
AWARENESS	When mistakes are revealed to you, you adjust accordingly.	You blame others for your mistakes.
	You seek first to understand, then to be understood.	You avoid healthy conflict by running from it or winning the argument.
CONNECTION	You practice being vulnerable with appropriate people in your life.	You relentlessly point out when someone does something you don't agree with.
	You intentionally find time to actively listen to others.	You tend to view others as being in your way on your road to success.
BOUNDARIES	You consistently try new things that help you stretch and grow.	You say no to everything.
	You take a stand on what matters to you and those you serve.	You say yes to everything.
AGILITY	You remain appropriately calm when facing adversity.	You tend to overreact on small or less important matters.
	You are willing to change when you recognize the value to do so.	You consistently resist change even when it is obviously needed.

WHAT TO EXPECT AS YOU READ THIS BOOK

I would like you to consider this book as a sort of trailhead marker or general guide for your journey of developing and sustaining resiliency. Trailheads can mark numerous places, such as the beginning of your journey or an area to stop and rest. It may even lead to a difficult climb with a breathtaking view as your reward. Trailheads give you, the hiker, a sense of direction helping you to know where you currently are so that you can visualize where you want to be. If you want to be a resilient physician, then this book is a good starting place for your resiliency journey. It offers proven lessons for staying on that path and alerts you to inevitable pitfalls along the way. The quest for resiliency *is* a journey and will require a determination like that of a purposeful and steadfast hiker with a conviction to reach the summit, but with the mindfulness to embrace and enjoy the journey along the way.

Your resiliency quest starts with multiple trailhead options. You will use your own internal compass to determine which ones to start with. Each trailhead you take will put you on the path to resiliency. Keep in mind, however, that there are an infinite number of trails to travel and summits to scale, therefore you will *always* be on a path of resiliency.

Summits represent moments in time like graduating college, getting married, giving life to a child, running a marathon, or nabbing your dream job. While these are amazing triumphs for sure, you may wake up the next day with a bit less enthusiasm as you realize you have no idea how to live with a new spouse or bounce back from the physical agony of a 26-mile race. Achieving a milestone is not enough over the course of life. Accomplishing the goal of becoming a physician is a remarkable endeavor. Yet, basking in that moment, or even season, is not enough to carry you through the challenging days ahead of living in that profession. You have to stay on the path of resiliency to retain your sense of joy and wellbeing. Hiking your way into resiliency is my way of helping you repurpose your success metrics by focusing on the journey rather than the destination.

I encourage you to embrace the life you have right in front of you along with enjoying the adventure of reaching milestones like providing excellent patient care, building a great leadership team, or helping others advance their career.

With those types of milestones in mind, I developed a resiliency quest model, to help illustrate what I believe is essential to become and remain resilient. The model features the five primary learning areas (domains) that can lead you to a resiliency building journey. The five domains in this model are ***purpose, awareness, connection, boundaries,*** and ***agility.*** By adopting and applying these domains to your daily life, you will inevitably build a healthy resiliency muscle. This will allow you to have reserves in place to navigate adversity at a moment's notice. Trailheads usually mark the beginning of a designed hiking path. Similarly, I've named the resiliency quest domains, trailheads, since each can be considered a starting point for the journey of resiliency learning.

THE RESILIENCY QUEST MODEL

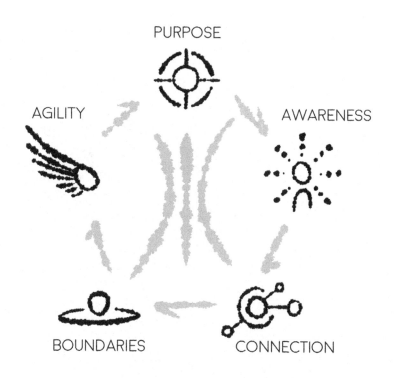

PURPOSE	Leads to values-based motivation.
AWARENESS	Leads to improving your power to choose.
CONNECTION	Leads to healthier relationships.
BOUNDARIES	Lead to more freedom to be yourself.
AGILITY	Leads to expanded openness to change.

PURPOSE TRAILHEAD

Purpose is what drives you toward your best self. Understanding why you do what you do will be a significant contributor to becoming and remaining a resilient physician. When you come face to face with adversity, knowing your purpose and allowing it to lead in the midst of that challenge will keep you on the path of resiliency.

Much of life is driven by needs and circumstances. You need to go to school to become educated. You need to have a job to pay the bills. You need to have a spouse, partner, or roommate because you don't want to be alone in life. To me, the choices you make about these types of circumstances are much more fulfilling when they are pulled by a purpose or goal than being pushed by a need. Which of your life decisions are being made on purpose? Do you know why you became a physician? Was it a response to a need such as pleasing your parents or teachers, or did you feel a deep calling before you even started medical school? Perhaps it was a true calling at the beginning but along the way became overshadowed by the urgency and pressure that accompanies your profession. In this instance, if you are able to recall your purpose for being a physician, or even establish a new one going forward, you are much more apt to be resilient and push through when change, chaos, and the unknown takes place because you know *why* you are doing what you're doing.

I strongly encourage you to choose to be on a resiliency journey. The 'rock and the hard place' circumstances, such as burnout, relationship failures, or deteriorating performance often produce the immediate push toward resiliency. While adversity can be a good teacher, living on purpose will give you a sense of autonomy allowing you to be a fully responsible contributor to your profession. Claiming your personal why will provide the source of inspiration and drive you will need to stay on your path. I realize that being this intentional is not for everyone and if your philosophy is to 'go with the flow' then that may be your own version of living on purpose. Either way you like to roll, I believe you will benefit from the following lessons in this trailhead that will serve as inspiration for living on purpose.

- SIMON BIRCH MINDSET
  Your mindset points to the direction you will go.

- SECRETS OF THE SEQUOIA
  Inner strength comes from knowing you are a part of something bigger.

- DON'T BE DECEIVED
  The enemy within can prevent purposeful living.

"When you stay on purpose and <u>refuse to be discouraged</u> by fear, you align with the infinite self, in which all possibilities exist."
~ Wayne Dyer

SIMON BIRCH MINDSET

"True happiness…is not attained through self-gratification, but through fidelity to a worthy purpose."

~ Helen Keller

Simon Birch is a character in a movie who reflects the idea that we all have a purpose in life if we choose to embrace it. The story centers around 12-year-old Joe Wentworth and his best friend Simon Birch, who was born with dwarfism. Simon believes that he was born different than his peers for a reason. He spends his brief life preparing for and attempting to discover that purpose. From a sequence of simple childhood games and extraordinary life circumstances, Simon ends up saving the lives of many young children by holding his breath for "200 Mississippi" and being small enough to fit through a tiny window in the back of a submerged school bus. I tell you this story to inspire and demonstrate the power of believing that your unique life has a purpose, and it is often much greater than individual pursuits and career ambition.

Retired from pro basketball, an amazing athlete and brilliant businessman, Kobe Bryant was extremely productive investing in the lives of his four daughters and in numerous entrepreneurial pursuits. Tragically, his dreams came to an abrupt end with the helicopter crash that killed the 41-year-old celebrity, his daughter, and seven other passengers. Along with the shock of this event, there was a general sense of sadness and distress that Bryant had just retired and was on his way to embracing the things he never had time to do at his day job of being a pro ballplayer.

A day after Bryant's accident, I turned to my wife and genuinely asked her that if I were killed in a plane crash in the midst of work travel would you/we be unhappy with how I invested time in my profession? The question led to a productive conversation about WHY I am doing what I do. Fortunately for me and my family we are clear about my purpose or calling. In short, I live a committed life. In my mid 20's I made the decision to live a life of faith. I believe I'm on this planet to serve and love others. I am grateful to have chosen my current path so many years ago. I am clear about my purpose, and thus align my passions, gifts, and desires in making my contribution. Like a chalk plumb line helps a carpenter in making precision lines for his project, my purpose aligns and guides me.

Do you recall the reason why you went to medical school? What drew you to explore medical studies? Maybe you loved science or math and that seemed to pull you in. Or perhaps you had a favorite relative who entertained you with fascinating stories of being a doctor? One physician I worked with grew up on a ranch and was always captivated by the natural process of being born and dying. I have had many conversations with physicians who have early childhood memories that are thematically shaped around hospitals and/or people being sick and needing help. Whatever drew you into medicine likely had something to do with a deeper calling in your life. Something unique to you. A small voice inside your head that continued to speak and shape your thinking.

I have heard that part of applying to medical school includes writing a personal statement on why you want to be a physician. Below is an excerpt from a candidate's personal statement to get into medical school. As you read, I invite you to think back to your promptings of being a physician and the excitement of applying to medical schools you were hopeful to train at.

"It is hard to separate science from medicine; in fact, medicine is science. However, medicine is also about people—their feelings, struggles and concerns. Humans are not pre-programmed robots that all face the same problems. Humans deserve sensitive and understanding physicians. Humans deserve doctors who are infinitely curious, constantly questioning new advents in medicine. They deserve someone who loves the challenge of problem solving and coming up with innovative individualized solutions. I want to be that physician. I want to be able to approach each case as a unique entity and incorporate my strengths into providing personalized care

for my patients. Until that time, I may be found Friday mornings in the operating room, peering over shoulders, dreaming about the day I get to hold the drill."

Do those words trigger any memories for you? I hope so. Your recollections are a tapestry of clues that can help you recall your personal WHY or PURPOSE. I encourage you to pull out your personal statement and read it. Marinate on the words and reflect on them until that spark is noticeable again. If the spark is noticeable, find a way to fan that spark into a flame. A physician asked his wife to read his statement to him and simply listening to it revived his purpose. You, and likely your friends and family, made huge sacrifices to get into medicine. Be shamelessly committed to the vocation that calls you and has your name on it. That calling will be an internal resource for you the rest of your career if you allow it to be. Understanding possible choices, making sound decisions, and being forward focused all happen more readily because you are clear and living on purpose.

One way to live on purpose is to know why you do what you do. Simon Sinek, author of *Start with Why*, has nearly had his book title become a household catchphrase. His passion is infectious, and his message is useful in reconnecting you to your why. Normally, I encourage people to avoid why questions. They tend to put you back on your heels rather than compel you forward. However, asking why in this context helps you become reflective rather than reactive. It is hard to believe that this tiny phrase can unlock the key to you living a meaningful life, but it often does.

Being on purpose or knowing your why is fundamental and critical. We are creatures that crave meaning. You need to know that your actions, work, and life matter. For example,

- A soldier needs a mission.
- A student needs a connection to learning.
- A teacher needs to influence the next generation of educators, doctors, and scientists.
- A lawyer needs a cause to fight for.

- A janitor needs to know cleaning bathrooms matters to someone.
- A physician needs a patient to care for.

If you cannot connect the dots between your life activities and a broader purpose, you will become apathetic and may drift into boredom, selfishness, anxiety, depression, or neuroticism, just to name a few. Drifting into useless human activity is easy. Being on purpose takes forethought and effort. Therefore, I encourage you to consider that your life is more than just a biological result. Your life really matters. Meaning and purpose have a natural place in your existence. Reducing yourself to being a passive participant in this investment of time marginalizes one of the best features of humans, your need to grow, create and thrive.

Expanding upon this need is what Sinek calls the Golden Circle. He suggests there is a natural sequence of life that works from the inside out. The inner circle represents *why* we do what we do, the next ring out represents *what* we do, and the outside ring reflects *how* we do what we do. Simply put, your *why* influences your *what* and your what shapes your *how*. For example, you decide to become a physician to improve healthcare in under-resourced communities. To fulfill your reason for becoming a physician, you focus on pediatric care by educating new mothers. One way you do this is by offering a free class on newborn care and reduced cost follow up. Ideally, understanding your why and having it fuel your what and how will lead you to more fulfillment in your career. People who live out their career from a place of fulfillment will be significantly more resilient than those who don't.

The movie Simon Birch is loosely based on a true story about a boy who overcame being a social outcast by choosing to believe there was an important reason for his uniqueness. Simon lived his brief life from a place of fulfillment. May we all be so fortunate to leverage our unique strengths into a force for good and ultimately a worthy purpose.

So, I ask you. What drives you? Why do you do what you do?

SECRETS OF THE SEQUOIA

"If you would know strength and patience, welcome the company of trees."

~ Hal Borland

Know who you are and why you exist. This knowledge can meaningfully shape the trajectory of your career. When you are around others, take note of those who are on purpose and are well connected. I am motivated by those magnetic people in my life who inspire me. I am also frequently inspired by nature. When I step foot into the presence of the staggeringly old Californian trees known as the Giant Sequoias, something unexplainable occurs. I get the sense that I am among the ancient of ancients. Time seems to stand still as I take in these amazing living structures. The secret to their resiliency is the combination of strength and connectivity. The Giant Sequoias are among the oldest living one stem organisms in the world with an underground network of roots that bind them all together. While visiting Yosemite National Park a few years ago, I became entranced with learning more about and from these enormous living creatures. The Giant Sequoias, and trees in general, have long been examples of steadfastness and resilience.

I believe nature is the undeniable teacher of resiliency. Storms such as Hurricanes Katrina and Andrew are recent examples of the powerful laws and lessons of nature. We accept that storms are not in our control, but we have learned to prepare for them. Notice I said prepare, not prevent. Contemplating storms inspired me to shape the understanding of resiliency around this lesson from nature, starting with how nature rebounds from being damaged to the resiliency of those who are victimized by its demonstrative power. Found right in the middle of most storms, trees are salient examples of resiliency. In the midst of extreme weather, resilient trees are the ones that stand strong, bend with the wind, or otherwise adapt to the circumstances. They can grow on rocky mountain tops, in between concrete sidewalks, or in the midst of gale-force winds. Trees, these amazing living entities, know how to survive and thrive despite challenging conditions. Physicians often find themselves in similar situations and need to learn how to grow and stay firm despite *their* challenging circumstances.

I observed this lesson taking place after a medical program was shut down due to compliance and safety issues. Under new leadership, I watched the seeds be planted, buds emerge, and new life begin. The first step was to find competent leadership, the second was to surround the leader with a talented team, and third to begin to do the work competently. Within months the program was reinstated where it eventually thrived and competed with much larger programs nearby. With some outside coaching, competent leadership, and engaged staff, this disaster became a flourishing forest of possibility. Even though the perfect program was not created, the team worked together to create life from death.

You probably learned in school that each year a tree forms new cells arranged in concentric circles called annual growth rings. According to dendrologists, trees always grow. Their rings show up in dry seasons and wet seasons. A long growing season with enough moisture results in a wide ring while a dry season will result in a narrow ring. In the same way, physicians who are in the best environment with the most nurturing elements will likely learn and grow more easily whereas physicians in a less nurturing environment may experience burnout, discouragement, or lack of inspiration. During a physician's dry season, growth is less noticeable and productivity wanes. Even so, growth is still taking place with many opportunities to become more resilient. I worked with a physician who was on the path to a promotion when his wife was diagnosed with cancer. He was fearful of anyone knowing about this upheaval in his personal life, as it may suggest he was no longer focused on his job. The increased stress quickly led to work performance derailment. For long periods of time, he was on the verge of burnout. After months of working together on his inflexible privacy boundary, he found the courage to share his personal challenge with his boss. A new trust was formed between the two of them and he was able to make adjustments that allowed him to juggle both his home situation and work demands.

Resiliency is the capacity to overcome difficult situations and spring back stronger. Like the Sequoia's resiliency secret of being strong and connected, as a physician, your resiliency can also grow from living on purpose guided by your own inner strength and a healthy connection with your network of peers. Facing strong winds and fire, these trees overcome and rebuild a new forest, a new life. You are taught in the solemn silence of the forest that, like them, you can also change, move forward, and overcome hardship. Like nature teaches, you can become part of a resilient community of your peers. You can help each other create new opportunities, ideas, and inspire growth within each other. You can become stronger by embracing new versions of yourselves and each other. That is the value of purposeful resilience and one of the many life-giving lessons of the Giant Sequoias.

DON'T BE DECEIVED

"One who deceives will always find those who allow themselves to be deceived."

~ Niccolo Machiavelli

Becoming resilient and maintaining a resilient life are going to be challenging like any goal, but in ways you may not be predicting. In reference to resiliency, adversity is often due to misconceptions or the cognitive errors you experience. If your end goal is healthy patterns of living, then you may have to undo some of what life has inadvertently taught you. The enemy within you is often more difficult to overcome than most external threats. You have heard the saying, "you are your own worst enemy." I work with many clients who deal with internal sabotage thinking, along with beliefs that are not conducive to a growth mindset. So, I've highlighted below a few mental deceptions that prevent you from being on purpose. I don't want you to be sidetracked by this faulty thinking any longer. If you are not aware and do not take steps to overcome them, these deceptions may prevent you from being your best self and cause you to struggle with resiliency and thriving.

DECEPTION 1: I MUST BE HAPPY

Most people believe that to experience a good life, you must be happy and fulfilled. Think of the last time someone asked how you are doing. If you are like me, the temptation is to say "doing great" regardless of whether that is true. In our culture, if you are not happy you may be doing something wrong. Perhaps the lie that many choose to believe goes something like this: people who have their 'act together' are happy; people who don't are not happy. Therefore, you have to pretend to be happy all the time because you don't want people to think you don't have your act together.

A 2017 Harris Poll reported that 33% of people stated they are happy. Does that mean that two-thirds of the country are unhappy? Not necessarily. The crazy thing about happiness is that it ebbs and flows rather than being constant. Gretchen Rubin, author of *The Happiness Project*, suggests that happiness is not really a choice, but rather a commitment to moving in a direction that reflects what is perceived to make one happy. She maintains that sleep, for instance, is a predictor of happiness. Most people need about 9 hours of sleep per night. How many 9 hour sleeping nights have you logged in the past year?

Daniel Gilbert, author of *Stumbling into Happiness*, suggests there is no perfectly reliable tool to measure a person's happiness, so researchers rely on the honesty of self-reporting. His research led him to the conclusion that imagination is what fails people. Because people imagine the future poorly, they in turn do not have access to what might make them happy. Maybe happiness is something you can aspire to, but not consistently experience. If that is true, why do you put pressure on yourself to be happy all the time? That state of being is unrealistic and almost like saying, I want it to be sunny and 75 degrees, regardless of where I live or what season it is. I urge you to not fall prey to this deception. Your value and reputation are not dependent on your ability to be happy.

DECEPTION 2: I MUST BE BUSY

How often do you hear "I am so busy" or "I am slammed" over the course of a day? While these comments should point toward the disease of workaholism, the behaviors these comments reflect are rewarded as a sign of being successful. Until this lie is exposed, many healthcare workers and physicians may eventually burnout from the disease of busyness. Busyness is not a sign of success but rather a symptom of a success delusion. Janet Ruffing in her article entitled, "*The Demon of Busyness*," proposes that busyness is a state of mind and a habit of the heart rather than merely a result of the number of tasks to be accomplished in any specific time frame. So, if you have the compulsion to stay busy, ask yourself, "what is the mindset and heart habit that might be driving my busyness?" The answer may be found in the words, "I must stay busy." Perhaps you have been misled to think that because you are busy, that makes you important. While it may not be at the forefront of your mind, there does seem to be a tendency toward this misguided thinking.

In my clinical experience, when people start a sentence with I must, it usually means that someone or something outside of themselves is driving their agenda. They have lost their personal locus of control. Self-dialogue might sound like, "I must be extra nice to my colleagues." What will happen if you are neutral, instead of nice? Who will even notice? "I must be on time or else." What will happen if you are not on time? Who is going to be the judge and juror if you are a few minutes late? "I must go to college." Really, who says? The idea that you must do anything is worth revisiting if you are prone to this type of thinking

According to Ruffing we have a limited number of positive words for the practice of not being busy. Mindfulness has emerged in the past decade as a potential candidate, but even that has mixed reviews among healthcare professionals. The challenge is that unless you value the practice of not being busy and instead possibly view it as rest or restoration, you will continue to view it as either being lazy or wasting time. Frankly, we usually value getting things done too much to even consider *being* rather than *doing*. I hope you will reconsider your definition of success and not permit this lie to deceive you into being distracted and too busy to be a healthier version of yourself.

DECEPTION 3: I MUST DO IT ALONE

Do you prefer not to ask for help when you are in need? You are not alone. Most people either decide or default to going it alone. Despite the wisdom from our greatest historical thought leaders, many are inclined to turn down help. The poet John Donne wrote that "no man is an island unto himself." People do not do well when they isolate themselves. We need each other to lean on, learn from, and hold accountable. Rugged individualism was a term invented in the minds of leaders facing the great depression. The idea that we need to 'cowboy up' or 'pull up the bootstraps' implies that doing life alone is expected. There are times when you have to show grit and determination to move forward in life, but in no way does that imply you have to do it alone. Just imagine if physicians around the globe decided that they didn't need any help. You simply can't do it all by yourself. Unfortunately, when it comes to managing your emotional and psychological wellbeing you tend to do just that. In our current culture, I believe needing help or asking for it is still viewed by most as a sign of weakness. Don't permit this deception to truncate the impact, value, and power of being vulnerable with your colleagues.

Remember, life ebbs and flows and is filled with adversity and challenges of all kinds. Don't allow these 'must deceptions' to take over your thoughts and actions. Determine to be self- honest, rest when necessary, and invite others to help you along the way. Doing so keeps you on the path of resiliency. Your purpose deserves your clearest thinking, focused pursuit of your goals, and pure motivation to be excellent.

HIGHLIGHTS OF THE PURPOSE TRAILHEAD

SIMON BIRCH MINDSET:
I am clear about my purpose, and thus align my passions, gifts, and desires in making my contribution. Like a chalk plumb line helps a carpenter in making precision lines for his project, my purpose aligns and guides me.

SECRETS OF THE SEQUOIA:
Resiliency is the capacity to overcome difficult situations and spring back stronger. Like the Sequoia's resiliency secret of being strong and connected, as a physician your resiliency can also grow from living on purpose guided by your own inner strength and a healthy connection with your network of peers.

DON' T BE DECEIVED:
In reference to resiliency, adversity is often due to misconceptions or the cognitive errors that you experience. If your end goal is healthy patterns of living, then you may have to undo some of what life has inadvertently taught you. The enemy within you is often more difficult to overcome than most external threats. You have heard the saying, "you are your own worst enemy"....Don't allow the 'must deceptions' to take over your thoughts and actions. Determine to be self-honest, rest when necessary, and invite others to help you along the way.

PURPOSE ACTIVATION

PHYSICIANS LIVE ON PURPOSE AND PRIORITIZE THEIR
LIFE ACCORDINGLY.

- They know who they are and why they do what they do.
  Without purpose the work can become meaningless; without
  priorities the work can become overwhelming.
- Because they are on purpose, they experience and express
  gratefulness.
- This attitudinal shift from complaints to gratefulness is
  transformational.
- The likelihood of burnout is very low when living on purpose
  and enjoying a constant mindset of gratitude.

PURPOSE PROTOCOL

PROFESSIONAL ASSISTED ACTION

- Retain a professional coach. Knowing and living out your
  purpose is so important that it is worth investing in a personal
  coach or an experienced mentor. There are a variety of options
  to consider when selecting a coach. We are providing a free
  coach selection consultation to anyone who reads this book.
  Our Resiliency Quest network administrator will review
  your needs and objectively recommend at least two different
  options for you to consider. (Note: this offer from the author
  is not intended to obtain personal referrals, so he will not be
  on the list) Please contact us at TheResiliencyQuest@gmail.
  com and ask for our coach referral network administrator.

SELF-DIRECTED ACTION

1. *Map your path:*
   Explore answers to the following questions. Lay the answers out on a table and map them to establish a thematic goal for your life.
   - What drives/motivates you?
   - What energizes you?
   - What you are willing to sacrifice for?
   - Who do you want to serve?
   - How do you want to serve?

2. *Create clarity:*
   My experience with physician leaders is that most of you have a pretty good idea of what your purpose is. The following questions are to assist you in uncovering or clarifying your purpose:
   - What drives you? When do you feel most engaged at work?
   - On days that you feel most alive and made a difference, what were you doing?
   - If you were no longer working in your clinic or department, what would they miss most about you?
   - When you were a child, what would your parents, teachers, or relatives say repeatedly about you?

3. *Read a book:*
   Read *The On Purpose Person* by Kevin McCarthy.
   - Follow his methodology for uncovering your purpose.
   - Share the book with a friend and uncover your purposes together
   - Hire a coach to help you implement your new learning (refer to the above for direction).

AWARENESS TRAILHEAD

Awareness, or specifically self-awareness, is the ability to see yourself and others clearly and as objectively as possible through self-reflection and introspection. Being self-aware gives you more access to choices and opportunities that can shape your life and career in a positive and meaningful way.

Most likely your career thus far has been about learning and growing in your role as a physician. Do you ever stop to remind yourself that there is a unique person who encompasses that role? That person is you and there is an infinite amount of curiosity, possibility, and passion within you. Perhaps you already know this about yourself, but if not, I encourage you to expand your self-awareness. Taking the time to reflect and invest in a relationship with yourself is illuminating and rewarding, however, it often gets replaced with the need to prove yourself to someone or something else. You are the only 'you' on the planet and it is *good to be you*. Being aware of this reality frees you from the judgment that you may place on yourself. If you want to be a physician who transforms failure into learning and insight into change, you need to have an increasing awareness of your patterns and convictions. If you are willing to explore your best self, that insight can be leveraged into better choices including the choice to be a more resilient human being.

The following lessons provide more understanding into the domain of awareness and how you can grow in that area.

- WINDOWPANES:
  There is more than one version of yourself; invest time in learning about your other sides.

- INNER TRUTH:
  Draw the line and take a stand.

- PRE-SCRIPT-IONS:
  The first place to look for what makes you tick are your patterns.

"Self-awareness gives you the capacity to learn from your mistakes as well as your successes. It enables you to keep growing."
~ Lawrence Bossidy

WINDOWPANES

"Don't accept your dog's admiration as conclusive evidence that you are wonderful."
~ Ann Landers

Receiving information and feedback from others, while important, can often be tricky to discern as it battles for place with our already preconceived thoughts and beliefs. It's not easy to potentially alter or leave behind information you believe to be true of yourself. It reminds me of car windows. When you are driving fast on a highway, what is in front of you is far more important than what is behind you. Windshields are sized and designed to keep you looking forward the vast majority of the time. On a much smaller scale, rearview mirrors are used only occasionally to check what is behind you. Do you tend to spend more time in front of the mirror studying what *has been* rather than addressing what *could be* in the present and/or future window right in front of you? What a self-limiting force those metaphorical mirrors can be! For some of you, it is more familiar and comfortable to remain in constant relationship with where you have been, seeing yourself in the mirror of life, than with boldly looking out the window of new possibilities.

In the 1950's Joseph Luft and Harrington Ingham studied this occurrence and created a tool often used called the Johari Window, named by using a combination of both their first names. This instrument is great for raising self-awareness, especially for those who work with frequently changing groups of people.

The Johari Window cleverly illustrates that you have four windowpanes through which you can understand yourself. Most people believe they are fairly self-aware. As I've worked with physicians, I've experienced that some of you consider yourselves more self-aware than most, yet in reality you struggle to really understand who you are. There are many reasons for this, but the most likely contributor is that you have no other point of reference to hear otherwise. Outside of your medical school training you probably don't receive much feedback. Even a suggestion that a windowpane model to achieve self-realization might seem unnecessary to you. It is not that you resist this idea conceptually, rather you simply haven't spent the time to consider the various versions of self that exist for you. If you choose to try it, the application of this tool can significantly heighten your awareness of the multiple vantage points involved in being in relationship with your colleagues, family, and friends.

The Johari Window tool highlights self-understanding in four ways The first pane is the *Arena* area, the public version of yourself. Facts that you and others are readily able to see and are routinely willing to share are part of your open or arena quadrant. Examples are: "I am a physician who works at ABC Hospital," or "I'm married with two children," or "I drive a minivan." Most people are comfortable with this area and rely on this dimension to be known, sometimes relying on it too much though. They may solely fall back on this windowpane to avoid revealing the other three quadrants. Be aware that some people dispute even the obvious facts about themselves. This may be a sign that they have significant self-awareness gap issues. If you or someone you know struggles with accepting this level of reality, it may suggest the need for professional intervention as this windowpane is the foundation of a comprehensive view of yourself.

The second pane is called the *Blind Spot*. The blind spot is perhaps the most misunderstood of the four panes. Any aspect that you do not know about yourself, but others within your peer group consistently notice and verbalize to you, is likely in your blind spot area. For example, as a physician leader you may feel like you handle conflict well, but in fact team members point out that you often avoid messy conversations that require you to show up and be direct. Without recognizing your blind spots in a humble and vulnerable way, you will continue to be unaware and miss out on fulfilling connections with others.

The third pane is the *Hidden* area. This refers to traits about yourself that you are aware of but may not want others to know about. People also refer to this quadrant as the secret area. If you have a concern about being exposed or shamed, you will compartmentalize this area and the information remains closed off to others. Still, there is an insatiable desire for others to know about another person's secrets. Your colleagues may be prone to making up stories in their minds about the information you choose to keep hidden. Perhaps doing that makes them feel better about their own kept secrets. I remember working with a physician leader who intentionally kept her personal life extremely private. I was in a casual conversation with her colleagues one day and heard a comment about this private physician "having trouble at home." I was curious so I asked what led them to make that conclusion. Responding with uncomfortable chuckles they admitted there was no evidence, but because she was so guarded the assumption was made that she was in a fight with her spouse or something similar was taking place. I recall wondering which was more unsettling: their jump to conclusions or the reality that this physician was so guarded that her colleagues felt the need to make up stories to relate to her. Navigating this tension is what makes you feel so uncomfortable. You may be aware that holding back is impairing your relationships, but you are unwilling to take the risk of being vulnerable. However, your willingness to be more open will influence how much and how often others choose to trust you.

The fourth windowpane is called the ***Potential*** area. This space reflects those characteristics that are unknown to you or anyone else. This aspect of the self encompasses things like abilities that are never realized or a fear or aversion to something that has never been encountered. Take marriage for example. As a single person, you have your set of ideals that you live by. Then you get married and are thrust into a whole new set of conditions that push you out of your comfort zone and into new and unfamiliar thoughts and behaviors. I like to refer to this window as the one that keeps us all humble. We just never know how we might react or behave given a circumstance we have never faced. Therefore, this perspective will keep you humble and vigilant as you encounter new experiences.

You need to keep in mind that you have many vantage points from which you can assess your personal value. That is why the Johari window is so important. The way you view and relate to yourself is integral to how you perform at work and home. Having a healthy and positive perspective of who you are and what you do is frequently associated with how successful you are. Have you ever considered that what you think of yourself is most likely different than what others think of you? For instance, you may be that person who attends a meeting thinking it's going to be a waste of time because you already know what it's going to be about. So, you go, unprepared to contribute, simply to check it off your list for the day. Your team members quickly pick up on the fact that you don't want to be there by the simple fact that you barely say hello and proceed to check texts and emails. Consequently, you've made the error that this meeting was to serve you by giving out information you thought you already knew, when in truth, it was an opportunity to serve the organization and your peers with your knowledge and opinions on the topic. What you are unaware of, that your colleagues continue to experience, is that you often show up to meetings in this way. It is a blind spot for you.

Being a physician, you are often on center stage and may be challenged with self-awareness questions from others. It's imperative to a successful working environment to be aware of your interactions with peers and patients. A familiar expression is: "How can you be so blind? Why can't you see what everyone else already notices about you?" These words may not be verbally directed at you but be assured you are certainly casting doubt in your colleague's mind if you are not demonstratively aware of your blind spots. Just as important as knowing your blind spots, I want you to be vigilant about recognizing your bright spots. These are the aspects of you and others that are naturally desirable qualities. Far too often you will tend to overlook the positive aspects of who you are because they may come easy to you. The following story illustrates how strengths, or bright spots, may be covered up by your blind spots.

Several years ago, I was retained by a department in a healthcare organization. My assignment was to work with a physician who was known for his competent work, but equally known for being behaviorally aloof and peculiar. Let's call him John. During our first meeting John asked me how many physicians I had worked with and for how long. I responded by asking him how that information would benefit *him* in his development discussions. He rambled on for a bit and I again confronted his need to know my work history. I reminded John of who referred me to him and why our meetings were necessary. I also conveyed that if he was not comfortable with me, I totally understood. After pausing for a moment and with a sheepish smile, he proceeded to tell me his story. Toward the end of the meeting, John promptly said he would be the best client I ever had. In essence, he believed he was going to make both of us look good.

The specific thing that happened next is what is most worth sharing. John asked me what he would have to do to become my best client ever. To me this was a very insightful question. I proceeded to tell John that the most effective way people can become better is through the often painful journey of self-awareness. John's response was, "got it, I can do that...and how hard can that be? I already know myself quite well." If you asked John today, he would tell you it took around two years of our work together to help him realize that he, in fact, did not know himself quite well and that by understanding the blind spot windowpane and increasing his self-awareness he was able to become a less aloof, more productive, and relationally engaged physician and colleague. In our work together I leveraged the power of a 360-feedback tool to anchor my point. A formal online assessment, the 360 provided feedback from superiors, colleagues, and direct reports. In essence, it was a 360-degree perspective of John's workplace behavior. The combination of the 360 data and my coaching questions assisted John in concluding that he in fact did not realize his own blind spots. By admitting his gap in self-awareness, he was then open to accepting his bright spots which included enthusiasm and helpfulness, and found more enjoyment in leveraging those strengths into positive interactions with his peers.

If you are similar to John, you may ask yourself, do I really have to learn more about this very basic human capability? The answer is yes. Isn't self-awareness implicit and everyone knows you have to be self-aware to be successful in life? The answer is no. Take driving in hazardous icy conditions for example. It would be a mistake to assume that people who live in cold, snowy areas are automatically good at driving in bad weather conditions. In fact, numerous drivers tightly clutch their hands on the wheel and creep along the snowy roads without paying attention that there are tips and warnings to guide them, such as: Stay off the highways during a severe snowstorm! Similarly, self-awareness is a life skill that you have to be vigilant at practicing in order to be masterful in any kind of environment, especially healthcare. Like learning to drive safely under poor conditions, self-awareness is a combination of common sense, fierce commitment to reality testing, and cumulative learning by trial and error.

I am convinced that increasing your self-awareness is a non-negotiable precursor to any and all sustainable development that will happen within you. Author and leadership development guru, Kevin Cashman, put it this way, "Personal mastery (self-awareness) is about comprehending the vehicle, our character, that brings us to our destination. There's just one problem; we've temporarily lost the 'owner's manual." And yet, we have to 'drive' to get anywhere in life.

Consider shrinking your self-awareness gap by using resources such as The Johari Window to increase your self-understanding as well as provide you some insight into how to practice listening and empathy with others. When you live transparently and are open to feedback from all four quadrants, you will experience less interpersonal conflict, enjoy your workplace relationships more, be able to lean into your strengths, and be considered a more approachable and engaging colleague. All of these keep you on the path of resiliency. Put simply, self-awareness is understanding who you are, how others experience you, and how you are similar to or different from other individuals.

INNER TRUTH

"I want my inner truth to be the plumb line for the choices I make about my life, about the work that I do and how I do it, about the relationships I enter into and how I conduct them."

~ Parker Palmer

After reading the Palmer quote above, you may be asking yourself, "what is my inner truth, and what is the connection to a plumb line?" These are invaluable questions to ponder as they serve as personal advisors to your behavior, whether you are aware of them or not.

So, what is inner truth? How do individuals know what their

inner truth looks like? Through my work with physicians like you, reading the great thought leaders of our time, and years of personal reflection, I have found that inner truth is something to uncover, not discover, because it's already there. Sometimes, it may be buried beneath many layers of denial or shame. Perhaps you excelled in school and were subsequently pressured into becoming a physician by your parents or other authority figures in your life, even though you felt led to pursue the arts. Now, you may feel embarrassed about not being honest with yourself and those who influenced you, so you remain silently miserable. Other times, your inner truth may be paused in order to save face in sticky circumstances. It is inner truth that gnaws at you when you realize you have not been forthright with the facts of a situation. I believe there are many paths to uncovering inner truth allowing it to lead. They all include being vulnerable, admitting your mistakes, and giving and receiving forgiveness.

To illustrate, I have witnessed tense conversations between physicians accusing situations such as not rounding on the patient properly, inaccurately charting, being racist, blaming other peers, and more. There is definitely low trust in these scenarios. It may be due to one physician believing her version of the events is unequivocally correct. Or the other physician knows he made an error but attempts to cover it up to save his reputation, or perhaps both simply do not know how to articulate their versions of the truth in a transparent and straightforward way. More times than not, individuals are aware of making a mistake so why not own up to it? Instead, accusations are made and conclusions proclaimed without having uncovered the true facts. The better path forward is to become vulnerable with each other, admit mistakes, forgive, and then invite each other to figure out the solution together. To illustrate, a physician blamed a colleague for not charting properly in the prior shift. She soon uncovered that she had made an error in judgment. She chose to go to her colleague and say the two magic words, "I'm sorry" which she followed with "I was wrong." Together they uncovered that the page was mistakenly removed and placed in another part of the chart. With only a few words, the power of that apology broke down the barrier between them, thus repairing the damage from the accusation. If you don't uncover your inner truth, that which leads you to do the right thing, and apply it in these types of situations, you will likely rely on excuses, blame shifting, and even lying to avoid looking bad. One approach leads to freedom, the other to ongoing problems.

Remember that everyone is unique, and thus each person's inner truth will be expressed in various ways. I have heard it said this way, "no two people see the same rainbow." I trust you can embrace the notion that your filter in part informs and shapes how you uncover your inner truth. Truth is truth, but my version of the truth may require you to listen longer before jumping to conclusions. Of course, I need to do the same for you. I know the term plumb line is not commonly used, but it serves as a wonderful word picture for how you can align yourself appropriately with your standards and values. Essentially a plumb line is found when you look within and understand what it is that drives you to do what you do. Webster defines a plumb line as "a vertical line." Your plumb line represents a congruent path from your inner truth to living out your purpose. For example, in order to build your dream home, you need a set of blueprints from which to build your foundation. Can you imagine framing rooms and erecting stairs without a base to connect them to? Similarly, in healthcare you need to know why patients are in the hospital before doing rounds on them. You probably look at medical records before meeting them. Then, you may order tests and/or labs and review them. Next, you most likely listen to the presenting problem from the nurse, and then proceed to treat your patients. These are practical examples of knowing what you need first, and then following a plumb line of data to determine the objective and plan.

It is mind boggling that many people live their whole lives doing things, without having any idea about why they are doing them. A lot of time and talent may be wasted when you are not clear about the direction you want your life to go. I am even more baffled when highly educated, morally trained, and emotionally mature individuals do things without any sense of why they do them. For instance, when I encounter physicians who are MD-PhD or MD- MBA, I ask myself if they take the extra training because it is simply available, someone told them to do it, or they genuinely want to pursue a career that will utilize both degrees. I confess, the first decade post grad school, I was unsure of my own career path. Being young, I had only vague notions of what I was doing or why I was doing it. Circumstances dictated that I snap out of it and put forethought and effort into my calling if I was going to have any chance of making an impact going forward.

I imagine you have colleagues who feel lost, or perhaps you do as well. You may have become a physician because your parents or heroes insisted, or maybe you dreamed of having a financially lucrative career. Now as a practicing physician you may find yourself wandering and confused because you did it for your parents or for the money and not as part of your master plan to be on purpose. It is never too late to get back on track, or to find a track for that matter. Purpose sets your trajectory and has built in resiliency to sustain it. If you feel yourself zig zagging through life, start by determining the plumb line that will help carry out your purpose.

A sure way to determine your plumb line and thus live out your inner truth is to lean into your values. I frequently notice people zoning out when talking about values, meaning the level of importance one places on something. Almost as if values are considered to be those nice to have, but not need to have, resources. On the contrary, awareness and practice of our values are essential. Like hardware inside a computer processor, you and I are programmed to have our own internal language. Your internal language leads to the creation of your values. To uncover what matters most to you, choose between overlapping values. For one to be more important you have to decide it is your priority. For instance, when you ponder the important traits you feel that you possess, like kindness, integrity, or self-control, ask yourself if you could only choose to live out one of them, which would you choose and why? For example, do you value honesty more than kindness? How about creativity or perseverance? This process quickly peels back the layers of contradiction that often clouds your thinking. It is possible that people avoid this type of reflection precisely because it causes them angst to be aware of what they find more important with their values, convictions, ethics, and desires. Most people don't take the time to contemplate what it is that really makes up who they are and how they can express that to the world. Rather they default to living according to external cues and trusting what others convey is appropriate.

To share a personal example, I was raised in a fundamental Christian home and that meant attending church on Sunday morning, Sunday night, and Wednesday night. The beliefs I was surrounded by seemed to be based more on following principles and rules than on freely living out a faith. As I became an adult it was important for me to determine if those beliefs were a part of my own path or if I was just adopting my parent's convictions. You may have your own version of a faith or family values story. Regardless of being in a church or in a healthcare setting, people tend to give their power away to external sources. Ask any member of a large organization why they 'work for' or 'belong to' said organization and they will frequently stutter and stumble their way into some explanation that is often far removed from a 'personal why' answer. For instance, ask a physician who works for XYZ hospital why he is a part of that organization and he may say, "it was where I trained so I found a home," or "it is a prestigious medical facility." Any way you slice this question you will likely get a 'should say' answer. I don't believe the intent is to deceive anyone, but rather he is unclear as to why he pursued working with that organization. I strongly encourage you to revisit the values that govern your behavior and choose to work with an organization that aligns closely with your chosen values.

Nursing is a noble profession and often attracts those who want to pursue living out their values. Over the years, I have had the privilege of working with many executive level nurses. One in particular stands out to me. During a conversation with her, she conveyed that while her career had not been an easy one, it was still very rewarding. I asked what led her to that conclusion. She eloquently spoke to me about how her work lines up with her values and what she may have called her 'inner language.' She felt congruent. Her role, her values, and her mission were all aligned. That didn't happen by accident. She had clearly explored and constructed some healthy patterns for herself.

I hope you can find that same clarity about your work. I encourage you to take the time to clarify your own values, align them with your talent and skills, and then put them to work. Being steadfast with your inner truth and the values that shape it will keep you on the path of resiliency when faced with both simple and daunting challenges. I will end this lesson with the same quote I started with. Read it again and ask yourself if the important choices in your life are reflective of living with intention and integrity.

"I want my inner truth to be the plumb line for the choices I make about my life, about the work that I do and how I do it, about the relationships I enter into and how I conduct them."

~ *Parker Palmer*

PRE-SCRIPT-IONS

"Self-Awareness is one of the rarest of human commodities. I don't mean self-consciousness where you're limiting and evaluating yourself. I mean being aware of your own patterns."

~ *Tony Robbins*

Part of your job as a physician is to write out prescriptions for your patients. The Latin word for prescription is "take thou." Prescriptions give the pharmacist permission to dispense medication for a patient to take. These scripts regulate what a patient needs to do. Psychologists have uncovered that when growing up a similar process occurs between a child and caregiver. Constructed by generations of parents, family scripts are the rules, both silent and spoken, that help guide you in how to live your life. These scripts become internalized and practiced without much awareness and acknowledgment that they even exist. In the same way you prescribe what a patient should do or take, from early in your life parents, mentors, other caregivers and close friends have shaped or 'prescribed' how you should act and be. Unless you take time to reflect on the accuracy and benefit of these scripts and make any necessary changes, they will simply live themselves out in your life.

Around the age of 14, I began to be curious about why people act the way they do. Unfortunately, this new curiosity came about from my family being in the middle of a crisis that ended in my parents getting divorced. This rocked the world of the four McKinley children, ages 5-17, and created a deep void leading to an unsettled inquisitiveness in me. The curiosity was driven mostly by my need to seek clarity and understanding about the pain and confusion this situation rendered. I was devastated at the time, but quickly converted my pain into leverageable capital: the kind whereby you can say to your Dad, "I am at Joe's house" and to your Mom, "Joe is with me here at Dad's house." Of course, this meant I literally didn't have to be at my mom's or dad's, and they were both ok with it. Doing exactly that ended up being a really fun time with friends one night, until I came home the next day to find out my grandpa had suddenly passed away while I was out doing my own thing. Consequently, my parents were out looking for me all night so they could pack up and get to my grandma's house to support her. You can imagine how horrible I felt at the panic I triggered. Because I blamed my parents for getting a divorce and causing my pain, I thought that entitled me to do whatever I wanted. My grandpa's death snapped me out of that and made me realize how selfish and unaware of others I was. Going forward, this experience helped keep me from having a negative life script of blaming others and taught me a lot about selfishness and being aware of other people.

I often hear from physicians that during the impressionable years of their childhood someone in their family was sick and/or in and out of hospitals. I recall one physician in particular. His mother had an extended illness which required having healthcare workers come to their home and care for her. He remembers sitting by her side watching them invest in his mother and was inspired by their generosity and kindness. His mother formed a bond with a few of those caregivers and my client 'witnessed the magic' and wanted to be just like them. When asked about his early memories (or scripts) he could not recall a time when he didn't want to be a physician. Fast forward 40 years and he is now meaningfully engaged in (his scripts) practicing medicine, passionate about his work, and connected with me to expand his clinical skills into leadership skills. Another physician I worked with told me he was in and out of the ER as a kid with all sorts of childhood and sports injuries and he remembers thinking that the medical provider guys have a cool job. Eventually he was accepted into medical school and when it came time to focus on his specialty area, it was an easy decision. These positive stories are inspiring and great examples of playing out a constructive life script.

I thoroughly enjoy helping physicians seek and find more self-understanding about their life scripts. I use self-report assessment tools like the DiSC®, MBTI®, and Enneagram® to assist in that endeavor. These are exceptional assessments that illuminate underlying personality and behavioral preferences and have found their valuable place in development programs around the world. Nearly every time I introduce this type of self-report tool to healthcare providers, they genuinely find it beneficial and insightful. Physicians love data so being able to show them patterns or graphs seems to grab their attention and lend credibility. Not only do I use these tools with clients, I also work to modify my own behavior with the insights these types of assessments can provide.

There are three insights that assessments can offer for people who want to understand themselves and others better. They are knowing your preferences, understanding your patterns, and paying attention to your overall profile and the profile of others. Unfortunately, people tend to live their lives without paying attention to the obvious patterns and preferences that are at play in shaping their behavior. So, investing in these types of assessments that reveal so much valuable information can increase awareness in self-limiting scripts and reinforce making better choices while being more empathetic with yourself and others. The overall goal is not for you to be driven by your scripts or personality, but rather allow you to leverage those patterns to assist you in fulfilling your dreams and aspirations and enjoying healthier relationships and a more satisfying life.

Scripts can play a major role in many aspects of your life. Robert Brooks and Sam Goldstein wrote a whole chapter about them in their insightful book, *The Power of Resilience*. According to the authors, "negative scripts serve as powerful obstacles to a resilient life. They tend to increase conflict with others." You would be wise to be mindful that they do exist. If you intend to live intentionally, rewriting these scripts are of utmost importance. I know you, like me, want to believe that you are open to new ideas, are flexible in your thinking, and emotionally agile enough to endure anything. However, we sometimes fail to show up that way when the moment arises. It is very easy to be seduced back into childhood training, despite our education, hours spent in therapy, or career success.

Recently, I was talking to a physician about a particular script she has. She engages with her co-workers in a very vulnerable and authentic manner until she feels she has completed her mission. Regardless of how the coworker feels, she moves on. We called it her mechanism. After exploring it together we uncovered it originated from her childhood experiences. She concluded at an early age that if she was bored with others, she would just ignore them. When she made the connection between her childhood and her current behavior she said, "well there you have it, now what do I do?" For sure, insight alone does not produce change, but it is a good starting point.

Remember life scripts can be used to build you up or break you down. There is no longer any reason for you to be empowered by the negative ones. You have access to many positive scripts, like becoming a physician because of a fond childhood association with the medical field. Below is encouraging data that reflects this shift in your mindset. In their research, Brooks and Goldstein found that there were positive scripts that supported a resilient mindset. These are ones that I find useful:

- I feel in control of my life
- I know how to restore and refuel my positive energy
- I lead with empathy
- I practice clear communication and prioritize my interpersonal skills
- I approach and solve problems and make decisions skillfully
- I set realistic goals and manage expectations appropriately
- I understand that both success and failure are my teacher
- I consistently practice compassion for my micro and macro community
- I value responsibility and act according to my claimed values
- I seek to live free of shame and accept myself and others as they are

I invite you to pay more attention to what is driving your behavior. To help in that endeavor take an online profile, get some candid feedback, or simply notice a pattern in your behavior that is unusually powerful. Leaning into powerful scripts as listed above can provide you with more choices and inspire the pursuit of living with confidence and resilience.

HIGHLIGHTS OF THE AWARENESS TRAILHEAD

WINDOWPANES:
Most people believe they are fairly self-aware. As I've worked with physicians, I've experienced that some of you consider yourselves more self-aware than most, yet in reality you struggle to really understand who you are. There are many reasons for this, but the most likely contributor is that you have no other point of reference to hear otherwise. Outside of your medical school training you probably don't receive much feedback.

INNER TRUTH:
Most people don't take the time to contemplate what it is that really makes up who they are and how they can express that to the world. Rather they default to living according to external cues and trusting what others convey is appropriate... Being steadfast with your inner truth and the values that shape it will keep you on the path of resiliency when faced with both simple and daunting challenges.

PRE-SCRIPT-IONS:
Remember, life scripts can be used to build you up or break you down. There is no longer any reason for you to be empowered by the negative ones. You have access to many positive scripts, like becoming a physician because of a fond childhood association with the medical field.

AWARENESS ACTIVATION

Physicians are genuinely honest in the acceptance of themselves and others.
- Being honest with your appraisal of self and others will eliminate unwanted distractions.
- Seeking feedback from your peers is normal and necessary for your success.
- Understanding that you are not in control of outcomes permits you to take risks.

AWARENESS PROTOCOL

PROFESSIONAL ASSISTED ACTION

- Select and recruit a mentor and ask them to help you get to know yourself better.
- Take personality and leadership assessments to increase your self-awareness.
    o Contact our office at TheResiliencyQuest@gmail.com and request the self-awareness assessment package.
    o Through your work, ask if there are any assessments for self-development that are made available for physicians.
- Get a referral from a colleague or friend for a great psychologist or therapist. If you find a good one, commit to 12-18 sessions focused on self-awareness.

SELF-DIRECTED ACTION

1. *Ask for it*:
    Ask five people for feedback on three things:
    - How well do I collaborate or work with people?
    - What is your opinion of my competence in my line of work?

- Am I a coachable person?
- Gather data, review it, and then share it with three close friends. Ask them to help you sort it out and make sense of it. Build three simple action steps to work on improving those areas of opportunity.

2. *Identify your scripts:*
   Write out the answers to these questions and ponder the answers with a colleague or close friend.
   - What did my grade-school teacher tell my parents about me being a student?
   - What did I learn about myself in school between ages 12-18?
   - What did I learn about myself during college, or until year 25?
   - What did my first boss tell me about my work?
   - What would my parents tell their friends and colleagues about me?
   - What would my two best friends tell my parents about me?
   - What is beautiful about your flaws and imperfections?

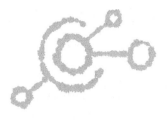

CONNECTION TRAILHEAD

Connection is about creating a psychologically safe work environment with your internal stakeholders, teams, and mentors. This safe environment accelerates your likelihood of experiencing a strong sense of belonging and acceptance.

You need to be in the community of others to be your best self. What is the point of doing life alone? Being connected is so much more than just having colleagues to work with, it is about enjoying being with them *in* the work. Connection is about risking being changed by being in a relationship with your coworker, family member or friend. The power of connection is the antidote to many of your life's deepest fears, like not belonging, being lonely, or feeling unloved. Thus, connection is intimately linked to being resilient. When you are accepted by your colleagues and are genuinely connected, your ability to face and overcome adversity exponentially increases. You can thrive in any adversity if you are part of a loving community of people you value, and who value you.

The following four lessons were written to equip you with ways to get and stay connected. I believe each one is uniquely suited to provide you with valuable resources.

- THREE WISE MONKEYS: What you see, hear, and say matters!

- LAW OF WILSON: You will benefit from having someone to help you solve problems.

- MULLIGAN PLEASE: Extending grace to your colleagues will go a long way.

- THE COURAGE TO BE IMPERFECT: Adaptive physicians are willing to work with people rather than control them.

"We cultivate love when we allow our most vulnerable and powerful selves to be deeply seen and known, and when we honor the spiritual connection that grows from that offering with trust, respect, kindness and affection."

~ Brene' Brown

THREE WISE MONKEYS

"I define connection as the energy that exists between people when they feel seen, heard, and valued; when they can give and receive without judgment; and when they derive sustenance and strength from the relationship….Courage starts with showing up and letting ourselves be seen."

~ Brene' Brown

You may not realize it but being connected to your peers is fundamental to being a resilient and thriving physician. I know it may not be intuitive to you and I am not basing this on anecdotal information. Brené Brown, a popular world class researcher, has established herself as the go to resource for understanding how people hide from each other and become known to each other. Her research has uncovered three things that people can do to overcome loneliness and become known and consequently engage in thriving. I am respectfully calling these the Three Wise Monkeys. The first monkey is being seen, second is being heard, and third is being valued. Do you recall the proverb: "see not, hear not, speak not?" It is often referred to as see no evil, hear no evil, speak no evil. While that may not have been the original meaning, to date one of the more popular understandings of this proverb is that we need to avoid dwelling on evil thoughts. I am inserting a positive spin on this proverb and applying Brown's insights to suggest we work harder to see others, hear others, and value others more intentionally. The Three Wise Monkeys are now on offense rather than defense. I encourage you to access them in your path forward to having deeper connections with your peers and key stakeholders.

PATH ONE: SEE OTHERS

The Zulu people are one of South Africa's largest ethnic groups. The greeting they use, along with many other locals in South Africa, is *Sawubona*. It means *'I see you.'* The Zulu people also believe that human beings exist only if others see and accept them as well. *Sawubona* literally means "I see you, and by seeing you, I bring you into being." Can you pause with me for a moment and comprehend that description? Because I see you, you now exist...wow. This could mean for you to be seen, you need to have a connection with see-ers. Fundamentally, your existence may depend on being connected.

The Zulu often respond to the greeting with *Shiboka* which means *'I exist for you.'* Both depict the importance of directing one's attention to the other person and being present. To be sure, the meanings of these greetings vary greatly from those heard most often in western cultures. "Hello, how are you?" is usually voiced without expecting a response and often without eye contact. If one does respond, it is frequently with "fine," which may carry the subtext of "I'm struggling, but I don't want to burden you, or share my pain." In our culture the reality is that we avoid being seen and consequently are limiting our ability for connection. Is it possible that you and I have just become accustomed to overlooking one another because we have habituated to that expectation? Is it really the best way to go about our days? While I don't think anyone intentionally chooses this approach to others, we often default to it which can lead to a perpetual cycle of feeling lonely. Well known author Robert Fulghum said, "And it is still true, no matter how old you are, when you go out into the world, it is best to hold hands and stick together" meaning we need each other and have the potential for an optimal life when we see and value each other as sojourners. Shifting from not seeing to seeing requires intentional effort. It is not easy and often does not come naturally to most people. Even so, amazing transformation can happen when you decide to make the investment. Several years ago, I had a friend who lamented about his wife not having a purpose since their kids were almost out of high school. He knew that my work often takes me into conversations with people who are in life transitions. He asked if I'd meet with her. I didn't know her very well other than exchanging pleasantries in social settings, and during those times I always mispronounced her name. So, while not knowing much about her and not even sure I would be helpful at all, I agreed to have a conversation with her. It wasn't long at all before I could sense her heart and envision a path forward for her that would play to her strengths. She thanked me for investing the time in her and we went on our way. It was one of those brief encounters that simply just worked and was very memorable for me. Fast forward many years later, her kids are both in college, she completed graduate school, has held a couple of jobs in the field, and is in her own unique way meaningfully connecting with people and the world. I was on a phone call recently with that friend and he made a comment to me that was surprising. He said, "my wife trusts you because you *saw* her in a way that only a few people have ever been able to see. I couldn't shake that comment. I saw her. It was immediately clear to me what he was saying. A person, whom he dearly loves and is closest to, was seen. That mattered to him and to her.

As you go about your day, are you in the habit of seeing your colleagues? Are they in the habit of seeing you? Do you feel seen? Who knows what you do and why you do it? I mean the good stuff, the real you. If you have such people in your life, it is likely they are treasured by you in many ways simply because they 'get you.' This wise monkey can be a catalyst for your resiliency currency. Burnout, depletion, and worse, clinical depression can all be linked to not being seen. Unlock this in yourself and others and experience the freedom from being seen. Additionally, being a physician who really sees their patients and their colleagues may be eminently more valued than one who does not. I can assure you that seeing others will translate to equity in your emotional reserve bank accounts. I know a physician who seems to know everyone by name, specifically hourly workers who appreciate it when he acknowledges them. As I walk around the hospital with him, I have a sincere sense that he has noticed these folks and cares about them as individuals. The currency that moments like this generate can be enough to sustain you during the challenging times. If you intentionally invest in your patients and others by seeing them, you will find yourself equipped for adversity and significantly more resilient.

PATH TWO: HEAR OTHERS

Intentionally connecting with another human being is one of the greatest things you can do, but there is often risk in doing so. Not being heard is the second of the three mistakes that Brown referred to in the opening chapter quote. It's important, yet sometimes tricky, when you put yourself out there and hope people can understand, care, and respond in some positive way. It's a wonder that you even try to make this happen given the odds of error that can take place. Nevertheless, you try but can often feel incomplete, and sometimes invisible, if you don't feel heard. I had a client who, one day out of nowhere, received a phone call from the company she worked for. It was the Senior HR person calling to let my client know she was immediately terminated and was to stop all communication with anyone in the company. She had practiced medicine for 20 years and had been a leader in her department for over 10 years. My client listened to what was being said to her, but she was not given the courtesy of being heard in return. Those close to the situation felt she did nothing wrong or unethical. She was just terminated. No severance, no explanation, no feedback of any kind, just terminated. Afterward she spent many hours with me talking through the struggle of not knowing this was coming and not having the chance to defend herself. This was devastating for my client. True, this was an extreme case of not being heard. Even so, being told what will happen with no opportunity nor acknowledgment that your voice matters can be incredibly damaging.

On the flip side, getting your 'day in court' to explain or express your perspective is extremely healing. As a clinician I worked for years with sexual abuse victims who were ignored, demeaned, and often abused for speaking out against their oppressor. I cannot describe to you the palpable healing that would take place for these victims when someone finally acknowledged that they were indeed abused. It released them from a bondage that amplifies this point. We all want and need to be heard.

What conditions need to be in place to be heard by another person? In the US Capitol Building there exists a spot where you can whisper to one another from yards apart and clearly hear each other. The room acoustics have to be just right as well as your position in the room needs to be accurate. Do you ever feel like you have to be in the right spot or feeling heard won't happen? I was talking to my colleague recently and he appeared distracted. Because he was distracted, I did not sense I had his full attention. I decided to wait until he could be fully present to continue the conversation. I did this in hopes of changing my position with him and thereby increasing the odds of being heard.

One of the key ingredients in people feeling heard is the act of listening, which is the active pursuit of understanding. For example, a nurse explains to the physician that their patient is still bleeding and uncomfortable, but all the physician hears is that he, the physician, did something wrong. The physician reacts defensively based on his impression of what is said, becomes frustrated, and rambles off additional orders. Yet, all the nurse wants is for the physician to know that the bleeding hadn't stopped so what should she do next? So, the nurse is left thinking: I speak, you hear what you want to hear, and I feel unheard.

I want to share with you a listening technique that can help you pay more attention when you need to. Being in a profession for over 30 years that requires active listening has fine-tuned that skill for me. Research, my experiences, and psychology theory inform me that there are at least three levels of listening. I am more convinced than ever that you and your colleagues would benefit from learning and knowing when to use each of these listening levels.

LEVEL ONE: HEARING

Physical hearing acknowledges that I hear a sound, or I hear you talking but I do not understand what it means. This type of listening occurs, for example, when you are on the phone listening to a colleague, but also responding to email at the same time.

Result: Audible hearing occurs but no understanding is achieved.

"You cannot truly listen to anyone and do anything else at the same time."

~ M. Scott Peck, American Psychiatrist

LEVEL TWO: INFORMATION GATHERING

I can repeat back to you what you said if you need me to follow your instructions. At this level I have no feelings about what you said, but I can repeat it back to you.

Result: I understand your request cognitively, but I am not emotionally connected to it.

"Most people do not listen with the intent to understand; they listen with the intent to reply."

~ Steven R. Covey, American Educator

LEVEL THREE: EMPATHETIC LISTENING

I care about what you are saying and your feelings about it matter to me. This level is the only level I think a connection occurs. Many people falsely assume they are connected to a person simply because they can parrot back what they say. Not necessarily.

Result: I hear you and am willing to risk caring about what you are feeling.

"Deep listening is the kind of listening that can help relieve the suffering of another person. You can call it compassionate listening. You listen with only one purpose: to help him or her to empty his heart."

~ Tich Nhat Hanh, Buddhist Monk

If you desire to make deeper connections with your coworkers, ensuring they feel heard will be important. A likely path to start that journey is to improve your listening skills. Developing a level three skill set requires intentional focus, practice, and desire. If you have work colleagues who want to share their experiences with you, consider hearing them out. Give their voice and stories a chance to breathe and have time to be contemplated. Be sure to ask if they want your opinion, or if they just need a listening ear. If you have a coworker who is tired and heading toward burnout, offer to have coffee with him, engage in empathetic listening, and watch him recover, often right before your eyes. It has been said that people don't need to get their way as much as they want and need to be heard. Even if you don't agree with everything they are saying, when you at least listen and consider their perspective, they can often recalibrate quickly.

PATH THREE: VALUE OTHERS

The way we value people and things tends to be very subjective. How do you put a value on that which matters to you? People tend to assume that everyone else should know what matters to them. I have not found that to be accurate. For example, there exists a TV channel that broadcasts car auctions of very rare and special cars, those that cost in the hundreds of thousands. Do old cars matter to you? They do to some. I was watching one time when a Ford Mustang 1965 Shelby GT 350 was being auctioned. It is widely regarded as the very best 'Stang' ever produced. I believe it sold for just under $200k. That's a whole lot of money. It caused me to wonder who felt the value of the vehicle was worth that much. The owner who may have had sentimental investment in it, or the buyer who was willing to pay whatever it took to get it?

I have personally experienced a valuing process known as a business valuation, whereby an external vendor performs a valuation on your company to ensure that a potential buyer doesn't under or overpay for it. Because I invested financial and sweat equity in growing my company, I believed it was very valuable and worth more than the valuation calculated. However, the reality is that "value" is not solely based on my perceived assessment, but rather on financial metrics, marketability, and what others have historically said a company like mine is worth. The truth is no matter how much you think your company is worth, it is only worth as much as someone is willing to pay.

Unlike buying and selling cars or valuing companies, I believe it is nearly impossible to follow a formula to guide you on how to value people as there is much more subjectivity with innumerable variables to consider. How do we value one person over another? A standardized way people are valued is reflected in the salary or wage assigned to roles within an organization. In your healthcare environment a nurse gets paid more than a technician, while a physician gets paid more than a nurse. It is very possible that individuals filling those roles may perceive their value based on what they are paid. The sad truth is that roles and people are sometimes one and the same in our minds leading us to value one person over another.

My conclusion to date is fairly straightforward. Whether it be a technician, nurse, or physician, when it comes right down to it you either value people or you don't. I mean that. People are unique and interesting and capable and fascinating. They can dance, create, speak, and build things. They have fascinating stories of where they grew up, what they've done, and places they've gone. There is simply no equal to the human race. People are valuable. If you choose to evade this concept, then I predict you will never fully connect with another person. Your interactions will feel more like a transaction instead of engagement. Further, when adversity hits, you will be hard pressed to be resilient without having the connection of others to encourage you.

Genuine connection with another human being requires empathy and understanding of an individual's greatest asset, being alive. Simply because you breathe, you have value. In addition, our culture suggests people can be measured by the sharing of their time, treasures, and talent. That is a great way to measure one's value, but also remember the value you give another person is often in direct proportion to the value you give yourself. Another way of saying this is, you can't give away something that you don't have yourself.

The Three Wise Monkeys concept is to help you remember that there are ways you can make deeper connections with people. If you agree with me that workplace relationships matter to your effectiveness, your resiliency and your joy, then start practicing these three skills. When they start working for you be sure to tell others what you are doing and why it is making a difference in your life. Everyone can benefit from understanding the impact of the Three Wise Monkeys.

MULLIGAN PLEASE

"Grace is the voice that calls us to change and then gives us the power to pull it off."

~ *Max Lucado*

Many years ago, a mentor shared with me the following proverb: *Give people what they need, not what they deserve.* I cannot think of any advice that has shaped my ability to love others more than this. If you want to be a physician who is known for having healthy relationships, you will want to embrace this idea and act accordingly in developing workplace relationships. You are often faced with the choice to either continue fighting for fairness with others or encouraging them to become better versions of themselves. This powerful principle can free you from falling into toxic relationships and instead set you up to be meaningfully connected with others.

The professional game of golf is well known for its self-governing ethics. When you make a mistake, it is expected that you 'turn yourself in.' As folklore goes, a golfer named Mulligan was delayed in getting to the golf course on time due to unforeseen circumstances. He rushed his first tee shot and experienced an unwanted outcome. Apparently, he negotiated with his golf buddies to get another shot without penalty due to his being rushed. That move has been coined 'taking a mulligan' and is frequently used in amateur golf. I have used it many times and find great relief in doing so.

I observe that most, if not all of us, need mulligans from time to time. We need to be able to reset and take another swing at life. Unfortunately, we usually find it easier to give ourselves a pass before thinking about doing it for others. We tend to hold each other to the letter of the law instead of giving each other the benefit of the doubt. Wouldn't you like to be a part of changing that unwanted pattern? What if you started each day accepting that extending mulligans is necessary sometimes and in fact could possibly become a way of life. Giving each other grace in this way is like giving a person gloves to wear on a cold winter day. You can make it without gloves in cold weather, but why would you want to? Grace allows for mistakes, oversights, sleepless nights, and thousands of other understandable explanations for not meeting expectations. To be sure, as physicians you know there are times when there is a low margin for error. Outside of those situations though, it is an act of grace to give what others need and not what they may deserve. If grace is not given, then both parties will be immobilized and not have the freedom to move forward and work effectively together.

Being stuck in this place will consume energy and emotion and thus trap both in a negative dance. Real teamwork does not happen when this dynamic is present. Frankly, we cannot collectively be effective if we don't give each other more grace.

If you believe people are fully responsible for their own actions, then you are likely inclined to think people get what they deserve, both good and bad. I advocate for taking ownership of our lives and believe you and I need to be fully accountable for our actions. There is no substitute for being a fully responsible person and professional. However, there are situations when getting what you deserve may seem unnecessary or extreme. If you drive 57 mph in a 55 mph speed zone, do you deserve to get a moving violation ticket? Technically you are violating the law, but should you get a ticket for a few miles over? Another example took place the week I was writing this section. A golfer hit his tee shot and due to miserable rainy weather, he could not find his ball. The rules say he only has three minutes to locate it. When he could not locate the ball within that time, he was penalized a stroke. A few minutes later someone found his ball buried in mud around the area they were previously looking. Even though the weather, not the golfer, caused the mud, the rules did not show any grace for such a situation. The golfer was held to the rules and not given grace despite not doing anything wrong or even making a terrible shot. Certainly, there are situations where it is necessary to follow rules, but there are also numerous times when discerning this proverb is very subjective. In those instances, maturity and context are required to apply it.

Basic essential needs are usually understood to be required for maintaining life. Water, sleep, food, and shelter are all examples of essential needs. I suggest adding grace to this list of essential needs. When grace is not extended for whatever reason, you may hear these phrases instead, "you got what you deserved, or you got what you had coming to you." While these responses may be the tendency, does it always have to end that way? There are some circumstances where natural consequences need to be permitted, such as getting burned when you touch a hot stove. However, if the consequences are at all subjective, why not offer grace to each other?

Do you remember the popular fable titled The Scorpion and Frog? To remind you, here is the story.

"A scorpion asks a frog to carry him over a river. The frog is afraid of being stung, but the scorpion argues that if it did so, both would sink, and the scorpion would drown. The frog then agrees, but midway across the river the scorpion does indeed sting the frog, dooming them both. When asked why, the scorpion points out that this is its nature."

The reality is that our basic nature is prone to want to 'sting' each other. However, giving people what they need, not what they deserve, invites you to overcome your basic nature and extend grace in certain circumstances. May you be one of those physicians who can help carry a colleague over the river and safely to the other side rather than one who stings.

LAW OF WILSON

"No sustainable change happens outside of a relationship."

No sustainable change happens outside of relationships. You can only truly know yourself by being in community with others who, throughout various interactions, constantly give you feedback and cues. Sometimes that feedback is blunt and difficult to hear. Other times it may be positive and affirming. More often though, the responses you receive from being in relationship with others may cause you to reflect and ask yourself if any changes must be made to get you to where you really want and need to be. Jane Dutton, researcher from the University of Michigan, refers to these exchanges as high-quality connections. She says, "The key to transforming the workplace experience is to build and nurture what I call "high-quality connections" – marked by mutual positive regard, trust, and active engagement on both sides. In a high-quality connection, people feel more open, competent, and alive." If you are going to be a resilient and thriving physician, this principle is going to be germane to your success. You cannot improve, change, and grow in isolation. When was the last time you received feedback from a peer, staff or a patient – or even a spouse or family member? Did you reflect or react to that feedback? You will need to experience high quality connections to be able to navigate tough times, face challenges, receive feedback, and pursue your goals and dreams.

When you think of relationships, you assume it is between human beings, which is predominantly true. However, I was reminded of the importance of having even the most basic of relationships when needing to make a change by watching the popular film *Cast Away* starring Tom Hanks. Chuck Nolan, the main character, was tragically cast away on a deserted island after surviving a weather-caused plane wreck. He was thrust into a survive-or-die situation with limited survival skills. He grasped for ways to overcome the lack of fresh water, food, and shelter. Of all the random wreckage items that happened to get washed up on shore, Nolan made use of a Wilson volleyball which came to life in his imagination and consequently became Nolan's companion and ultimate motivator. After reflecting on this movie, I recognized a change agility principle within the story and named it **The Law of Wilson**. It is defined by my opening comment of this lesson. No sustainable change happens outside of a relationship.

Near the end of the story Nolan sought shelter in a cave due to the monsoon season. The most salient scene that reflects this principle came when Nolan was in a heated debate with Wilson on how to maneuver a makeshift raft over incoming waves generated by the overwhelming tide. Nolan made a final stand and convinced Wilson (himself) that they should go for it. This decision to 'change the tide' of his circumstances is what formed the basis of this principle: Nolan needed the energy that was created from his *relationship* with Wilson to dream, innovate, and inspire himself to find a way off the island in hopes of being rescued by a passing ship. It gave him real hope. The storyline of this film creatively illustrates how relationships and community are needed in our lives, even when it is fabricated with an inanimate object.

Humans are known to nurture themselves by becoming attached to or in relationship with many non-human alternatives: cars, houses, geographies, or pets. We all know how important those relationships can be, but none can compare to the potential power for positive change that a willing, self-aware, and wholehearted human being can provide for us. Human relationships are the cornerstone to becoming more self-aware. I am very fortunate to be in a relationship with my wife where we have learned to cultivate a dynamic exchange between us. She asks questions and challenges me based on her awareness of my fears and insecurities and I in turn do the same for her. This did not happen spontaneously. Over time we forged a psychologically safe environment for these discussions to happen because of trust and confidence in each other. In a similar way, workplace connections can offer both insight and motivation to become a more well-rounded health provider. When you are in meaningful relationships with other physicians, they will likely hold you accountable to your commitments, goals, and aspirations. "Iron sharpens iron" as the old proverb says. Who are you in relationship with right now that can be direct and honest with you? Are you open to their feedback? Are you willing to be a safe person for others? If so, that exchange of open and honest communication between you and others leads to more self-awareness which in turn leads to more growth and resiliency.

Some recent advances in brain research can help you understand how relationships can support you being more resilient and less anxious. Connections between people are commonly made either face to face and/or virtually. Research has uncovered that something wonderful and additive also takes place in your brain as you talk with others. This neurological shift is one of the best resiliency resources that no one is talking about.

Judith Glasser, a psychologist, has brought forward this idea in her best-selling book, *Conversational Intelligence*. She outlines the neurological effects of having a connection with another person. First, when you dynamically engage with others, the neural activity in your brain is different than when you are alone with your own thoughts. (Law of Wilson confirmed by science). For instance, I feel different when I am talking with my wife than when I am pondering a decision alone. Also, I feel different talking to my neighbor than talking to a coworker. Each conversation brings with it a unique experience. It's possible that connection with your coworkers may have many more benefits than you imagine. They can include feeling relaxed and calm, gaining positive energy from another person, and of course meeting the need to be needed, whether that means serving others or reminding you that what you do matters. You may realize that it is in those moments of deep conversation that the potential of experiencing respect and acceptance dramatically increases, which is definitely evidence of a high-quality connection.

Next, your brain mirrors another person's brain when in conversation. When two people are interacting and sharing information, the signals from both brains synchronize, particularly in language receptive regions. Literature has described how this 'mirroring' concept correlates with studies on the development of emotional intelligence. Essentially this suggests that when two coworkers connect in conversation, they can become neurologically synchronized. It's good to be mindful of who you choose to talk to. Working as a therapist I can attest to this experience. Clients would often come into my office very anxious and afraid and then leave with hope and optimism. I'd love to say this is because of my charming personality and savvy skills, but I know better! I believe it has to do with feeling connected to another person and ideally with someone who has a calm brain. If you see your therapist and he is more anxious than you are, you will not likely return to therapy. Conversely, if you visit with him and his calm brain allows you to relax and think through your issues more clearly, you are likely to continue therapy. Having those moments of synchronicity with another caring human being can be the difference between psychologically drowning or swimming to shore. You are capable of creating that connection with your staff and patients. It can be as simple as stopping to compliment a staff person's new hair style or thanking a floor nurse for adding value to a patient's care by going the extra mile to calm his fears. Your patients feel more connected when they sense you taking a few more moments to actively listen to their concerns and answer their questions.

Some call it political savvy, others say it is emotional intelligence, and some chalk it up to people skills. Whichever way you lean, the single common denominator of all three is the ability to pick up social nuances in conversations. Physicians are known for being great clinicians, but some are less adept interpersonally. Walking through the halls of a hospital or darting around an operating room, your staff are giving away social cues every day that can be overlooked or disregarded. Becoming skilled and intentional about noticing these cues will increase your interpersonal effectiveness. Many of my discussions with physicians end up with me encouraging them to increase the face-to-face conversations they have with patients and coworkers to improve connection. Eye-to-eye contact is a necessary social cue that has proven to make deeper connections. Mutual eye contact between two individuals activates in the brain, specifically the right temporal-occipital-parietal junction, a region sensitive to high level social cues. Glasser's research suggests that eye contact is the primary determinant that facilitates this type of connection. If you are looking at your phone while talking or listening and not making eye contact, you will be missing critical pieces of information that will inevitably lead to disconnection.

In many ways, your conversations are either creating trust or provoking distrust. This can leave you feeling good or feeling bad about yourself, or each other. Some may prefer not to engage in conversation and sit on the fence, holding back by choosing to wait and see. This passive stance does nothing but keep things stuck. It ends up being just another form of distancing from each other. When there is no connection, you may feel threatened and disengaged, protecting yourself from perceived harm by withdrawing to stay safe. On the other hand, when you take the risk to connect with someone else you are able to bond, grow, and collaborate with that person, which helps build rapport and trust. By understanding that your brain mirrors another's brain in conversation and paying attention to social cues, both your patients and coworkers will feel seen, heard, and valued by you more consistently. The ensuing result is increased resilience and greater positive impact on others.

Understanding the Law of Wilson principle has helped hundreds of people I have had the pleasure of working with. We are not designed to do life alone. If you want to become a better physician or just a better human, you need to invest in and courageously be vulnerable with some of your coworkers. Allow them to be intentional and truthful with you, which in turn, helps to increase your connection and self-awareness. If a beloved dog, a special vacation spot, or even a simple volleyball can inspire people to change and become better versions of themselves, just imagine what being intentionally connected with a colleague could do to increase joy and meaning in both your personal and work life.

THE COURAGE TO BE IMPERFECT

"Better to do something imperfectly than to do nothing flawlessly."
- Robert H. Schuller

At the turn of the 20th century one of my mentors, Alfred Adler, coined the phrase "have the courage to be imperfect." In his research and experience with people he believed one of the most treasured of all human capabilities is to have courage, and specifically the courage to not seek or expect perfection.

Do you struggle with perfectionism? This self-inflicted lie has become one of the more common energy drainers and entrapments for healthcare providers. Coming out of medical school and entering into the open competition of the healthcare field can definitely lead you to the temptation of needing to be perfect in order to stand out amongst your peers. Because medical school breeds discipline and perhaps perfectionism, you may tend to overvalue an accurate diagnosis and undervalue relationships. It is understandable given your training, however not ideal given your humanity and the need to get along with others, especially if you are to be perceived as a team player. Furthermore, you are not rewarded for being vulnerable when making mistakes, rather the focus is on making no mistakes, which is an unrealistic expectation and can be a source of physician burnout.

If you value being self-aware and thus have a better understanding and acceptance of your limitations, you need to be encouraged rather than discouraged to be yourself. Brené Brown has been writing about having the courage to be imperfect for over a decade now. She and her staff have effectively pulled back the curtain of denial on the neurotic need to be perfect. She has studied shame and vulnerability in depth and has discovered that vulnerability is directly linked to courage. Brown proposes you need self-awareness to be courageous. I flip that around a bit and say that to truly become fully self-aware, you need courage to take those scary steps into the unknown. Her research uncovered four skills that lead to courageous behaviors and are highlighted in her book, *Dare to Lead*. I explain them below to help you consider overcoming your need to be perfect, if that is your tendency, which will guide you in your goal of becoming more resilient.

VULNERABILITY is described as being willing to take risks without knowing the outcome of a situation. Are you willing to expose yourself by being vulnerable enough to hear feedback, internalize it, and change because of it? The story of John I shared earlier in Windowpanes illustrates one physician's lack of being vulnerable. At the beginning, he sought to convince me that he could change without any real effort or awareness on his part. I put it this way: you can't become *all you want to be* without knowing *who you* *really are*. The starting point for self-honesty is in fact practicing vulnerability with yourself and others.

VALUES based living refers to your need to live from the inside out. If you are clear about your values or things that are most important to you, then you are much more inclined to lean into new experiences and bravely face new opportunities. I notice that people are generally reluctant to prioritize what they value because it may force them to choose between two equally important values. Often the one you're not prioritizing at the time is the one that others expect you to live out of. For instance, which do you value more, honesty or kindness? Your value for kindness may lead you not to tell the truth to your co-worker about her messy medical record documentation. Or your value of honesty may lead you to angrily express your feelings about her being five minutes late. You are most likely exposing a psychological blind spot when you are not clear about your values or don't understand why you are expressing one over another. The reluctance to intentionally choose what is most important to you prevents you from being clearer with others about who you are and what you stand for.

BRAVE TRUST is the foundation for all relationships. It takes courage to risk trusting people. Trust doesn't seem logical when faced with the certain likelihood of being disappointed. Even so, you need to be brave and lean into trust. Your relationships depend on it. Many people have the belief that trust should be earned. I would emphatically disagree. I believe mistrust is earned and that trust is given. Certainly, earning trust is a convenient way of having that confidence, and puts the burden on the other person to perform, but most of the time trust has to be given to others in order for human imperfections to be handled effectively.

LEARNING TO RISE has become Brown's go to skill set. She demonstrates that this skill is essential to be a fully functioning adult. Just imagine if you didn't know how to get back up after a physical fall. You would never attempt to walk the same way again, always in fear of falling. Emotional falling can create the same sort of irrational belief and subsequent behavior. "If I get knocked down, I will never recover, therefore I will simply not put myself out there." You will discover with more reflection that this skill is wildly important in not only *becoming* fully aware but also in *remaining* courageously self-aware.

So, what does it look like for you to have the courage to be imperfect? Start by investing in a meaningful relationship at work or home. Perhaps you have a close friend that you have been overlooking or one you have been holding at arm's length for too long. Shoot them a text or email, or better yet, pick up the phone to check in. Meet for coffee to catch up. Keep pursuing even when you're uncertain of their response or you may not know the best way to connect. As in the Law of Wilson, when you take a chance on being in a relationship, amazing changes for growth can take place. Another way to practice courage in sharing your imperfect self is to reveal more of your hidden expressions with someone you trust. Likewise, be truthful with them about their own blind spots. Further, choose one or two of Brown's four skills of courage to begin developing a braver you. I have found that being vulnerable can open many doors into developing and sustaining healthy relationships that allow me to have the courage to be imperfect. I am also convinced that burnout and resiliency are inexorably linked to your expression of courage.

HIGHLIGHTS OF THE CONNECTION TRAILHEAD

THREE WISE MONKEYS:
My conclusion to date is fairly straightforward. Whether it be a technician, nurse, or physician, when it comes right down to it, you either value people or you don't. I mean that. People are unique and interesting and capable and fascinating.....Genuine connection with another human being requires empathy and understanding of an individual's greatest asset, being alive. Simply because you breathe, you have value.

MULLIGAN PLEASE:
"Give people what they need, not what they deserve." I cannot think of any advice that has shaped my ability to love others more than this. If you want to be a physician who is known for having healthy relationships, you will want to embrace this idea and act accordingly in developing workplace relationships.

LAW OF WILSON:
You can only truly know yourself by being in community with others who, throughout various interactions, are constantly giving you feedback and cues. Sometimes that feedback is blunt and difficult to hear. Other times it may be positive and affirming. More often though, the responses you receive from being in relationship with others may cause you to reflect and ask yourself if any changes must be made to get you to where you really want and need to be.

THE COURAGE TO BE IMPERFECT:
Do you struggle with perfectionism? This self-inflicted lie has become one of the more common energy drainers and entrapments for healthcare providers...you are not rewarded for being vulnerable when making mistakes, rather the focus is on making no mistakes, which is an unrealistic expectation and can be a source of physician burnout.

CONNECTION ACTIVATION

Physician leaders are comfortable and engaged in healthy workplace relationships.
- You practice vulnerability and empathy in your pursuit of connection.
- You are a good empathetic listener.
- You value people for who they are.

CONNECTION PROTOCOL

PROFESSIONAL ASSISTED ACTION

- Take the well-known Dale Carnegie course: How to win friends and influence people.
  o **www.dalecarnegie.com**
- Take the Leadership Development Program course at the Center for Creative Leadership.
  o **www.CCL.org**

SELF-DIRECTED ACTION

1. *Practice vulnerability:*
   Listen to this Ted Talk by Brene' Brown:
   https://mindfulnessexercises.com/brene-brown-power-vulnerability/

   Then practice these three things for a month:

   - Try admitting a weakness you have with someone each day or several times a week for a month.
   - Tell someone you are sorry when you overstepped your boundaries or did something that hurt someone you care about.
   - Ask for help at least two times per week for a month.

2. *Friendship Circle:*
   Evaluating your circle of friendships and categorize them into three categories:

   Level 1: these are people you enjoy seeing occasionally.
   Level 2: people you enjoy being with but don't find the time to be connected often.
   Level 3: these are true friends (most people only have 2-3 in a lifetime).

   Once you complete the three circles then assess if there are any level two friends that could be level three.

   > Design a plan to invite that person to a casual conversation in the next two weeks and explore if they have interest in being more connected. If I show that I need more accountability in my life and invite them to help, they are more inclined to engage in a deeper friendship.

   Assess if there are any level one friends that could be level two.

   > These are more difficult to determine so you will have to just identify a few of them and show more interest in being with them. If they respond, then make a gesture to spend more time together doing a fun activity.

BOUNDARIES TRAILHEAD

Boundaries are the psychological parameters that define who you are and who you are not. Your boundaries protect you from being easily distracted, becoming a victim of comparison, or pursuing a superficial version of yourself. They permit you to live out your own convictions and values.

Taking responsibility for your actions, feelings and behaviors is essential to be a resilient physician. While that may sound easy, consider the ways you may miss that mark. You really need to know what you are, and are not, responsible for. Further, you want to be an individual whose yes means yes and no means no. In your career, there will be those you work with who may want to make you responsible for their sense of well-being. They will easily blame you or insinuate you caused their pain or discomfort. If you do not have a clear set of personal boundaries, you can inadvertently take on other people's responsibilities and frustrations. This will leave you feeling drained, resentful, or burned out. Additionally, you can also become the one who blames others if you don't have a definite sense of your own boundaries. Either way, if you want to be a resilient physician then start by being clear about what you are responsible for and why.

The next four lessons are not subtle. The only way to have healthy boundaries is to make clear declarations. The following are snapshots of the many ways there are to set guardrails around your most valuable resources, specifically yourself.

- BOULDER AND THE BACKPACK: What you tolerate is what you will end up with.

- TATTOOS, ACCENTS, AND ATTIRE: Withholding judgment keeps you free to be yourself.

- PLAYING FULL OUT: Don't leave anything on the field...go for it within healthy perimeters.

- RIVERBANKS: The current of your life needs to be contained by thoughtful margins.

"Boundaries define us. They define what is me and what is not me. A boundary shows me where I end and someone else begins, leading me to a sense of ownership. Knowing what I am to own and take responsibility for gives me freedom."

~ Henry Cloud

BOULDER AND THE BACKPACK

"Your personal boundaries protect the inner core of your identity and your right to choices."

- Gerard Manley Hopkins

Self-regulation is the ability to manage your emotional and mental energy. Setting and maintaining your personal boundaries is just a form of self-regulation and something few people talk about. Imagine your responsibilities in life are represented by a backpack that you alone carry. You engage in your life and strive to be a productive member of society. The backpack and everything in it are yours to take care of. The *backpack* contents are things such as holding a job, paying bills, and maintaining a house. While these are some of the basics, there are also intangible things like using common sense, formulating and achieving goals, and experiencing equality in relationships. These and others take energy to create and maintain. If you are efficient with these responsibilities, you have some additional energy left over to manage life's inconveniences. The objective is to be as diligent as you can with the backpack contents, so you have enough energy when unforeseen challenges arise. That's the backpack, your responsibilities, your backpack. Like food and water, your backpack is essential and necessary for you to carry - at all times.

From time to time, however, you notice that life has somehow added weight to your backpack by dropping 'boulders' in it. Now, in addition to your normal day to day obligations and small inconveniences, you find yourself carrying an extra load. The original weight of your backpack is uniquely designed with your specific strengths and weaknesses in mind. It is in perfect balance with your unique capabilities. However, when adversity comes along, the weight of the added boulders can become crippling. These *boulders* represent major challenges like a cancer diagnosis, a sudden unforeseen and dramatic job change, your home being destroyed by fire, or a significant relationship failure.

Sometimes these adverse challenges immobilize you so much that you need to ask for help to lighten your burden. If you are fortunate enough to have friends and family to help you rally and are humble and willing to ask for their help, you will benefit from their assistance. And those individuals will in turn feel fulfilled in supporting you. If you are less fortunate and or not humble enough to ask for help, you will remain in distress trying to endure the debilitating toll of the extra weight. In addition, your friends and family will be robbed of the satisfaction that comes from serving and helping others in need. If you are aware and willing to learn, life will teach you when to take care of yourself and when you need others.

This analogy, shared by my good friend Jon, illustrates the boundary line between what is your responsibility and what may be out of your control, necessitating the need to ask for help. It also can teach those of us who are in position to assist, to learn when it is appropriate to help. The rule of thumb is that the backpack and basic contents are your responsibility. The boulders represent times to ask for and offer help. Unfortunately, I frequently witness misuse of these natural boundaries. Touching a red-hot stove will always lead to unwanted results - and the same applies here - not respecting the natural boundaries between backpack and boulders will cause you to get burned.

An example of this boundary in your healthcare world is the management of your clinical schedule. To illustrate, a physician's family member who lives overseas had a dire healthcare emergency and the physician had to leave the United States. She asked some of her colleagues to cover her schedule since she likely would be gone for a couple of weeks. Despite informing them of her need and situation, a few of her colleagues were not OK with the additional burden. They wanted to point out all the reasons why it wasn't fair to put them in this position. Had the physician asked for coverage because she wanted to attend her son's band concert for a few hours (backpack), the colleagues with a negative response may have been warranted in their opinions. In this case her mother was very ill, and she needed to go home and care for her for a few weeks (boulder). These types of subjective situations can create unwanted tension if not addressed with intention, skill, and language that both parties can understand. Professional and personal boundaries are essential to be effective at work.

Boundaries are also useful in prioritizing what is most important to invest in and protect. Picture the way you carry a cupcake with a lit candle to surprise someone for their birthday. You carry it with one hand and instinctively block the fire from any wind with the other hand. The fire becomes the most important priority at this moment. The cupcake flame is so fragile you have to walk very slowly and carefully to prevent the flame from extinguishing. That powerful energy source needs protection during a simple walk from the kitchen counter to the table. If you are able to think of yourself and your important priorities as that fragile flame with unlimited potential, you would do everything you can to embrace and protect that potential so it can be leveraged into an amazing life at work and home. Therefore, it is critical for you to know the difference between what is important and what is less important. Additionally, if you treat each other's priorities as a fragile flame, you might be more careful about protecting your coworker's flame and they in turn will more likely respect yours.

With your training and skills in healthcare, setting and keeping appropriate boundaries will unlock your unlimited potential. You are capable of leveraging that potential into changing the world, and in medicine that can be literal. As I write this, the world is in the midst of a global pandemic. You and your peers are throwing yourselves into either saving people's lives from this aggressive virus or researching and supporting to find a treatment. At some point, you or one of your peers will solve the mystery and discover a vaccine for this horrible killer, so don't be hesitant or unclear about what is most important in your life. Investing in the right priorities for the right reason will be a valuable asset.

The purpose of having boundaries is to create perimeters to protect and take care of yourself, and your backpack. You need to be skilled and prepared to say no to something, or to tell other people when they are acting in ways that are not helpful to you. A first step is knowing that you have a right to decide for yourself what is good for you and what is bad for you. You have not only the right, but the duty to take responsibility for how you permit others to treat you. Setting boundaries is not a way to manipulate others to your advantage. Some people will say they are setting boundaries, when in fact they are attempting to gain power and leverage. The difference between manipulating and setting a boundary in a healthy way is the motivation for doing it. For example, a selfish motivation for doing something may be to prevent someone else from regretting their actions. Psychologists tend to call this enablement. Or, you may say no to a course of action because you are simply just being lazy. If you say no for selfish reasons, it may create resentment in another person who then heads down their own selfish path. It can be a vicious cycle. Motivation for saying yes and no if kept pure will be invaluable to you. Use the power of choice wisely.

Your priorities need to be protected so as not to be extinguished. Some priorities include basics like getting a good night's sleep, which is often a problem for many physicians, or restricting alcohol or other substances that can put you at high risk for malpractice or even addictions. Remember the old childhood story about the Golden Goose? The tale highlights the importance of having access to the Golden Goose and protecting its health to ensure its gold keeps coming. YOU are the golden goose. Your life, your energy, your training and skills are what make you so extremely vital. Obviously when COVID-19 hit and all non-essential work had to stop, physicians were deemed essential. You were not told to stay home. You were mandated to show up to work every day. In fact, there was often a shortage of physicians during the early days because so many were taken out of service because of positive COVID-19 tests. It was devastating for your colleagues, the patients, and you. We simply can't afford for physicians to be out of service. Everything you can do to prevent burnout and sustain engagement in your work is non-negotiable. This is frequently referred to as your ability to self-regulate. Your work and life matters. The general population needs you to be able to fully engage and be your best self. We don't want you to be held back because you are depleted or beat up by our insatiable demand of your time. We need you to protect yourself from the things that will deter you from doing what is best for you. To help from becoming depleted, some of your peers choose to take more vacations, develop a hobby, or engage in a meditation routine.

Being a resilient and thriving physician will develop in many unique ways. Sometimes the most resilient physicians are just people who know who they are and what they are responsible for. They are owners of their own backpack. They don't blame anyone else for their own daily challenges and don't try to rescue others from theirs. They know when boulders are present and seek appropriate assistance. In essence, their resilience comes from having a healthy set of psychological boundaries as described in this simple analogy of the boulder and the backpack.

TATTOOS, ACCENTS, AND ATTIRE

"Never question another man's motive. His wisdom, yes, but not his motives."

~ Dwight D. Eisenhower

People want the freedom to be themselves, to make their own choices, and not be unfairly judged for either. When you judge other people, especially their motives, you expend unnecessary energy and potentially derail yourself from being your best. It may not be obvious at first but by diverting your attention and concerning yourself in other's affairs, you are in a way draining your own resources. You might notice that many people do things differently than you do and you need to be ok with that. Some of these things may in fact be offensive to you. Is that because the action itself is truly offensive or you think your way of seeing the action is the true and only way to see it. This is illustrated by my 83-year- old mother. Her ultra conservative upbringing taught her to have little tolerance for tattoos. Even after hours of conversation with her on this subject, she is reluctant to let go of her opinion that people who have tattoos are somehow less virtuous. Even though she may not be alone in her thinking, the reality is that tattoos are accepted as an individual's personal expression in our current culture. We need to practice more flexibility in our perspectives of each other and lay aside judgments that usually end up causing undue stress and disdain. Those feelings are not healthy, nor will they help you on your resiliency quest.

Maybe tattoos don't bother you but figuring out accents do. A thick accent can be challenging to understand and often triggers a negative response in people trying to listen. I have witnessed many misunderstandings from accents or language barriers. We are quick to judge the person we don't understand as being the problem, rather than the communication process itself as the barrier to overcome. In college I had a classmate from the South who genuinely did not believe he had an accent and expended a lot of energy defending that belief. He felt everyone else around him had accents. This is how most people feel when interacting with those from a different country. While most don't dwell on or get upset about accent differences, there are some who assume that how they were taught to speak is the proper, or best way, and that others should accommodate them. This is misguided thinking at its core. The best way to overcome this inaccuracy is to adopt the skill of listening for understanding instead of listening to be understood. If you feel misunderstood, it may be because you have not made the effort to create a genuine connection with whom you are speaking.

Attire or what people choose to wear is another commonly misunderstood or perhaps judged behavior. Lady Gaga was clearly branded by her infamous "Meat Dress" which she wore at the 2010 MTV Video Music Awards. I personally remember responding with "what is she thinking?" Later I read an article on why she focused so much on being different. It was very revealing, and I grew in my understanding of her motives. This is a great example of just how nonsensical you and I can be regarding attire. You have heard phrases like 'dress for success' or 'know your audience' and both are valid and useful ways to think about attire. Some workplaces require employees to follow a dress code, while some have general guidelines. Certainly, most people would not show up to a formal wedding in shorts and a Hawaiian shirt. The problem with attire begins when you frown on others, or worse judge them for how they choose to dress. Would you agree that not much good can come from judging another's clothing choices? Why not embrace the differences as just that, differences.

Samuel Johnson, the great 17th century author, suggested we cannot see our motives, only our actions. I have a long-standing conviction that humans are not in a position to judge each other's motives. I hold the belief that it is wrong to do so. You can think I made a bad decision and question the rationale or logic of it, but beyond that it is not your place to judge. If a physician misrepresents himself in documenting a patient file or misrepresents facts on a curriculum vitae or article, what does that mean about him? Is he a bad person or did he do a bad thing? Do you judge his behavior or the reasons for his behavior?

Why do people feel so inclined to judge each other anyway? It is counter intuitive if you think about it. If you go around judging others, it only makes sense that they will do the same to you. I would prefer to let your motives be yours and my motives be mine. Unfortunately, I observe people rushing to judgment far too often in healthcare settings. Especially when things go wrong, the tendency is to blame and shame.

Being judgmental is not a constructive stance to take with your colleagues. A helpful suggestion is to shift from making a conclusion to noting an observation. Having an observation simply implies noticing what is going on around you. When you draw a conclusion or judge another person, you are in essence entrapping yourself by limiting your choices. Judgment is often accompanied by frustration, agitation, and downright anger. It is almost as if you believe you have no choice in the matter other than to believe what you do. The reality is that you do have choices about your beliefs and behaviors.

Observation is a neutral act of witnessing the actions of others. For instance, you observe a man walk out of a store holding the top of a single brown bag. You may conclude that he is either walking out of a store with a brown bag in his hand, or an early morning cocktail. There is no way for you to know what is actually in the brown bag by simply observing him holding it. The act of observing something happening is merely being aware of an action. You move it to judgment when you infer the motive.

Think about how being judgmental impacts your chance for

being connected with another person. Connection is highly unlikely if you judge a person's motives rather than giving that person the benefit of the doubt. For some reason humans tend to believe the worst about each other rather than anticipate best intentions. It may have something to do with the internal struggle you have with navigating your own inner incongruencies or blind spots. Mazhsarin R. Banaji in her book *Blindspot* says: "Blindspots hide both discriminations and privileges, so neither the discriminators nor the targets of discrimination, neither those who do the privileging nor the privileged, are aware. No small wonder that any attempt to consciously level the playing field meets with such resistance." You can set out to do the right things your whole life and so often get off course and be disappointed in yourself. Many people call this lack of integrity, but I tend to name it being human. You simply cannot rely solely on yourself to be consistently free of judgment.

Gandhi was credited for the saying, "Be the change you want to see in others." I read this quote everywhere in books, articles, and slide decks. If this saying is true, why don't more people take the risk of changing themselves? The opposite is usually true. I hear things like, "why should I change if my enemy is not going to?" or "I am not making the first move" or my personal favorite, "I am not going to let them off the hook." These ineffective strategies simply give away your power. I developed a simple and practical replacement strategy which is to encourage people to replace their judgments with curiosity. If you make this trade, you can extinguish your judgment about any number of situations or patterns that you may encounter. And in the end, you may learn something and build a new muscle.

- **Rude behavior:** rather than judge, ask the rude person if you have done something to offend them.
- **Tattoos:** rather than scorning this art form, ask for the story behind the tattoo.
- **Introversion:** rather than judging others with this tendency, become curious about what prevents them from speaking up and the peace they must experience by not being involved in everyone else's drama.

- **Smoking:** rather than spurning people who smoke, ask them what is so enjoyable about the habit that they would be willing to go outside in subzero weather to partake of it.
- **Same sex relationships:** rather than rejecting, engage in a conversation with someone who loves in this way.
- **Sarcasm:** rather than wonder about this, ask the sarcastic communicator to explain what they mean by their comments so that you understand them in a less derogatory way.
- **Ambitious people:** rather than writing them off as greedy, ask them questions about their dreams and find out what makes them tick. You may have a newfound respect for their goal attainment value.

You have a choice. Jumping to judgment is simply a habit, not a cause-and-effect relationship. No one is born judgmental. Judgment takes years of practice and building layers of psychological callousness. If you believe that judgment is a choice, try this replacement technique. At a minimum, you will be enlightened with new insights. The power of this reversal is in the approach: when you make an observation, you avoid the slide into judgment. As long as you hold it as an observation, you are at full choice as to what you will do with that observation, and therein lies the power. Therefore, as you observe tattoos, accents, attire, attitudes, actions or anything else that may be different from what you personally prefer or find appealing, you can choose to be curious and thus free from the entrapment of judgment and a never-ending dance of drama which drains your emotional and psychological resources. Choose to observe and be curious and you will recoup energy and redirect your focus toward being the best version of yourself.

PLAYING FULL OUT

"Do what you love. Do what is important to you and your family. I just want to encourage people to just go for it and do what makes sense to you."

~ *Chip Gaines*

I design my life to be able to play full out. I use this expression often with friends, colleagues and clients. Simply put, it means I'm being present with my attention and focused with my intentions. Playing full out means that I am not going to leave anything on the court of life. I am going to go for it. Are you going for it? Since leaving medical school, have you pressed the appropriate accelerators of your life, or are you hesitating or doubting so as not to lose what you have accomplished thus far? Knowing who you are and what you are meant to do, then setting and keeping healthy boundaries is one way you can be free from the self-limiting beliefs and behaviors that can be so crippling and cause you to remain on the safe bench of life instead of playing freely on the field. Don't be held back by anything that is within your control. You are capable of managing your own internal reactions to the circumventing circumstances in life.

Last Christmas my wife and two adult kids gave me a pair of my favorite amazing shoes. They are so amazing that I couldn't get myself to wear them. By March I had only worn them two times for less than an hour each time. My wife chuckled at me one day almost as if to say, "and why did we get them for you?" I remember trying to figure out what I was waiting for. My thoughts ranged from I didn't want them to get dirty to they were too good to wear because they were more than I normally pay for shoes. I wanted them to be worn for special purposes only. Eventually I realized that was nonsense, so I decided to wear them for a whole day out. It was an amazing foot day! I enjoyed the feel, the look, the comfort, and support. I continued to wear them daily. In this simple illustration, I moved from a scarcity mindset and began to play full out by not waiting for a special moment to wear the shoes. I wondered about other special moments in life that I was missing out on by holding back the best version of myself. I don't want to wait for a special day to be me. I can be me anytime I choose to and so can you.

Over the years, I have been invited to work with the Chairs of departments, physician CEOs and chief medical officers. These are extraordinary people. They have become highly competent clinicians, productive researchers and educators, and incredible leaders. Their career progression is often a shining example of playing full out. They are leveraging the tripartite mission championed by all academic medical centers and are recruiting and influencing others to do the same. One such leader I was engaged with was always pushing the envelope. As a minority, she was born in a foreign country and immigrated to the United States to attend college and excelled and continues to excel at everything she does. While working with her, I reflected on my own career ambitions and was often motivated to write another book, train more coaches, or expand a skill set. She is truly inspiring. Further, she has several hobbies and does them well too. One thing she says is, "you can sleep when you are dead." She is not being literal, but rather refers to sleeping as 'coasting through life.' Coasting is not an option. She is pursuing everything she wants to and is not allowing outside noise to prevent her from being her best. She enjoys life to the fullest and is at peace with her choices.

High School football practices remind me of another lesson I learned about playing full out. In Saginaw, Michigan, on a very hot summer day, I was warming up on the practice field. I was doing jumping jacks while this epiphany hit me: "If I work hard during the practice sessions, I can increase my odds to play well under the lights on Friday nights." That self-discovery has proven to be a worthwhile principle to follow. Basically, if you are going to spend two hours practicing or doing anything, why not get the most out of it? I decided to be the first one to the field and exert maximum effort during conditioning drills and plays. Looking back, I understand why I was one of four players who played both offense and defense. Walt Disney said, "Whatever you do, do it well. Do it so well that when people see you do it, they will want to come back and see you do it again, and they will want to bring others and show them how well you do what you do." I don't recall being influenced by Disney at that time, but all these years later I realize that we have nothing holding us back but ourselves. So, get after it! Be who you dream of in your mind, and you will find yourself caught up in something wonderful that only you can create and experience. Live a life worth dreaming about.

One of my favorite inspirational quotes is by author Marianne Williamson. This phrase resonates with me at a deep level. I think she captures this idea of playing full out in a concise and powerful way. I will end this chapter with her words as they need no further explanation.

"Our deepest fear is not that we are inadequate. Our deepest fear is that we are powerful beyond measure. It is our light, not our darkness that most frightens us. We ask ourselves, 'Who am I to be brilliant, gorgeous, talented, fabulous?' Actually, who are you not to be? You are a child of God. You playing small does not serve the world. There is nothing enlightened about shrinking so that other people won't feel insecure around you. We are all meant to shine, as children do. We were born to make manifest the glory of God that is within us. It's not just in some of us; it's in everyone. And as we let our own light shine, we unconsciously give other people permission to do the same. As we are liberated from our own fear, our presence automatically liberates others."

RIVERBANKS

"The lines we draw that make us who we are, are potent by virtue of being non-negotiable, and even, at some level, indefensible."
~ Walter Kirn

By now you know that I am a fan of nature. From being amongst Giant Sequoias to hiking mountain trails, I often uncover gems of truth from observing nature. On one such hike, I was looking at a river and recognized that to be a river, it needs to have natural banks on either side that contain its current. The flow of that river was influenced by its origination, depth, and the distance the banks were from each other. This river observation became the inspiration of my prior company's strategic plan. My partner and I were defining our "why we exist" statement and ended up calling it the Riverbanks principle. Imagine the flowing river as the current of life. Every river has banks on each side. Think of these banks as boundaries that remind you to stay in the river, or the current of your life. The boundary banks are essential to inform you when you are flowing with the current of your work, or to warn when you are on shore, or out of alignment with your goals and values.

I experienced this principle as a freshman in college when my family moved to the west coast of Florida. The first thing my father did after moving to the Tampa Bay area was to buy a fishing boat. I had not been around water that much but remember being excited about learning the mechanics and navigation of boats. The 15-year-old 19 ft fishing boat with a 75-horsepower engine was nothing special, but to me, it was amazing. The first thing I learned was how not to create wakes in the channels leading out to the ocean. The second thing I had to learn was about the markers that guide the boat operator out to open water. The Gulf of Mexico is very shallow around the shorelines and often requires thoughtful navigation to get around the sand bars and coral to avoid damaging the boat. I quickly found out that you keep the red buoys on the right and the green buoys on the left when going out to the deep waters - and the reverse on the way back. These buoys were the 'banks' that kept me out of real trouble and ultimately led me in the direction that I wanted to go. What are your buoys that keep you in the right direction?

I encourage you to think about and create riverbanks for your life. Your inner truth needs to be encompassed by boundary lines. Within those boundaries, you have a lot of freedom to operate. Let's dive a bit deeper into this analogy. First, remember that water flows where the underlying structures allow it to. When you tip over a bucket full of water in your garage and the water spills out, it finds paths of least resistance and starts creating little river streams all over the floor which represents the lack of boundaries to channel the water. To fully and joyfully experience the current of your life, or your inner truth, you need to put structures, or boundaries, around it to ensure it flows directionally where you need and want it to go. Let's say you opened a private practice. Unless you inform the public of your specialty - your "practice riverbanks" - you will be overwhelmed by the unlimited medical issues that come through your door. In essence your value will be diluted by pulling you onto a riverbank that you have no experience nor interest in being on. Your real expertise will be leveraged into value when you define the boundaries that you want to work within.

Building riverbank boundaries begins by determining what the banks represent. On each side of the river decide what you will *not* do. I've been married for 35 years. On one side of the river, I chose not to explore any other intimacy that will distract me from my marriage. On the other riverbank, I chose not to do anything to or for us without considering the possible outcome for our relationship. So, one bank is being faithful to each other, and the other puts our relationship needs over our individual needs. These commitments are the two boundaries that keep my marriage flowing in the right direction. While other vows have guided us, these two have proven to be the strongest boundaries that have kept us from possible painful consequences. Certainly, as humans we all make mistakes and suffer the ramifications, and my wife and I have made our fair share. Even so, being vigilant about putting boundaries in place allowed us more freedom to enjoy the marriage relationship to the fullest.

All thriving physicians need to establish their deep convictions and in turn, use those convictions to inform them what to do. Know who you are and who you are not. Once you establish the non-negotiable boundary lines, you can swim freely in your vocational current. A reason to resonate with the riverbanks principle is the imagery of flowing freely down the river of life understanding that the current is something you can't control. You can only control what boundaries you choose to operate within, which in turn gives you the confidence to move forward in your career and life.

You may have heard the story of Desmond Doss. A movie about him was produced to highlight his ability to live out of his conviction by setting boundaries. His story reflects a mindset or personal conviction known as the Conscientious Objector. His life was guided by clear riverbanks around his personal conviction.

Doss felt strongly about not bearing arms against his fellow man, yet he wanted to serve in the military alongside his friends and fellow citizens in protecting his country. The idea of enlisting in the military yet refusing to use a gun seems unrealistic and illogical. Doss signed up, endured the rigor of base camp, became a trained soldier, and went into combat without having to compromise his conviction to not bear arms. He lived intentionally on purpose and remained relevant and respected despite not 'going with the flow' of expectations demanded of him by others. Doss was also able to be respectful to those who believed differently than he did.

I want to motivate you to construct riverbanks to guide your career as a physician. Do not settle for what your peers expect or what the vocation demands you to do. Being a physician on purpose in all you do necessitates deep convictions. Desmond Doss not only lived on purpose, but he also earned the respect of his comrades, saved numerous lives, was awarded multiple medals for bravery, and enjoyed a long life. Doss found a way to make a worthy contribution without compromising his values. One way to live out your values is to construct and commit to your own riverbanks. Choose the boundaries that you are not willing to cross because if you do, too much stress and potential damage will be caused. Know your convictions, set your boundaries and live within them, and you will channel your potential into real benefit for your patients, students, staff, colleagues and yourself.

HIGHLIGHTS FROM THE BOUNDARIES TRAILHEAD

BOULDER AND THE BACKPACK:
The rule of thumb is that the backpack and basic contents are your responsibility. The boulders represent times to ask for and offer help...Sometimes the most resilient physicians are just people who know who they are and what they are responsible for. They are owners of their own backpack. They don't blame anyone else for their own daily challenges and don't try to rescue others from theirs. They know when boulders are present and seek appropriate assistance.

TATTOOS, ACCENTS, AND ATTIRE:
Being judgmental is not a constructive stance to take with your colleagues. A helpful suggestion is to shift from making a conclusion to noting an observation. Having an observation simply implies noticing what is going on around you. When you draw a conclusion or judge another person, you are in essence entrapping yourself by limiting your choices.

PLAYING FULL OUT:
Knowing who you are and what you are meant to do, then setting and keeping healthy boundaries is one way you can be free from the self-limiting beliefs and behaviors that can be so crippling and cause you to remain on the safe bench of life instead of playing freely on the field. Don't be held back by anything that is within your control.

RIVERBANKS:
All thriving physicians need to establish their deep convictions and in turn, use those convictions to inform them what to do. Know who you are and who you are not. Once you establish the non-negotiable boundary lines, you can swim freely in your vocational current.

BOUNDARIES ACTIVATION

Physician leaders are clear about who they are and who they are not.
- Never give your power away to others, only to your purpose.
- Your personal brand and power are fragile and uniquely given to you for stewardship.
- Your power is not transferable, so in someone else's hands it becomes useless energy for both parties.

BOUNDARIES PROTOCOL

PROFESSIONAL ASSISTED ACTION

- Sign up for the Boundaries training by Henry Cloud.
  o www.Boundaries.me.
- Get a referral from a colleague or friend for a psychologist or therapist who is skilled at helping professionals with setting and keeping boundaries.
  o www.psychologytoday.com

SELF-DIRECTED ACTION

1. *Meditation mantra:* Rehearse these mantras until you can begin to internalize them.

   - I have a great job, but I am not my job.
   - I have been well trained, but I am not limited to my training.
   - I have a busy schedule, but I am not a victim of my busy schedule.

2. *The Power of No:* We all have those one or two people we cannot say "No" to for some irrational reason. Do it today!

)(

- Make a list of the people you don't say No to enough.
- Prioritize that list and commit to starting with the top one.
- Journal or talk to a colleague about the experience of saying No.

3. ***The Power of Yes:*** Say "Yes" to something new in your life. Think about things you wish you could be doing more of and make a list of them.

- Prioritize the top 1-2 things you want to say yes to.
- Consider inviting that new activity or person into your life and make a decision to do so when it feels right.
- Give it a go.

AGILITY TRAILHEAD

Agility is the change ability needed when you find yourself surrounded by ambiguity, uncertainty, volatility, and complexity. It is being flexible, adaptable, and quick on your feet when change is instantaneous or looms in the distance.

While you and I would much prefer certainty and predictability, it is highly unlikely as change is inevitable. It is a life constant. As a physician, I imagine that you are faced with a myriad of changes on almost a daily basis. I encourage you to embrace those changes when it is necessary to do so. By embracing change, I mean really diving in and committing to being adaptive and willing to do what is uncomfortable and sometimes even risky. People who fear being agile or avoid it are often those who believe there is only one way to do things. Leading with agility is a demonstrative example of being resilient.

The four lessons in this section reflect a variety of different perspectives on change and being more agile.

- MIND LIKE WATER: Keep your challenges in appropriate perspective.

- CIRQUE DU SOLEIL: Balance is dynamic and versatile rather than static and linear.

- ACTIVATION OF AGILITY: You will benefit by having an agility compass.

- CHANGE AGILITY HABITS: If you can change, anything is possible.

"Success today requires the agility and drive to constantly rethink, reinvigorate, react, and reinvent."

~ Bill Gates

MIND LIKE WATER

"Rough waters are truer tests of leadership. In calm water every ship has a good captain."

~Swedish proverb

I admire people who seem to absorb adversity as a natural part of their life. These are people who look cancer straight in the face, manage a divorce as amicably as possible, or navigate messy career transitions with fortitude. Even with these upheavals, they still find ways to be resourceful and move forward. These dynamic and resilient people are inspiring and give us hope that we can be overcomers as well. They exemplify the concept of Mind Like Water. Drawing from an ancient metaphor, mind like water illustrates how an individual responds to circumstances according to the level of gravity of those circumstances. Small problems cause a small ripple effect; large problems generate large ripple effects. David Allen, author of *Getting Things Done*, defines mind like water as "a mental and emotional state in which your head is clear, and able to create and respond freely, unencumbered with distractions and split focus."

One of the extraordinary capabilities I observe in resilient people is agility. It functions in a similar manner as mind like water. Agility is the skill that allows you to adapt swiftly in rapidly changing environments while maintaining priorities, values, and boundaries. Agility is a necessity for daily success in professional activities. Currently, you are faced with a very real example of this. You are being told to move from a fee for service model to a value-based care model. This paradigm change is dramatic and insists that you shift your thinking about how you deliver your care. You didn't ask for it, you likely didn't want it, but the changing healthcare landscape now requires you to adjust to it. You need to be agile in your thinking in order to stay on the path of resiliency.

As a physician you have had to face many changes and the concept of agility may already be familiar to you. However, mind like water agility is a bit different in that it reflects more of the inner emotional dialogue you are managing as opposed to navigating external environments. When you transition between patients, administration, staff, and insurance carriers, you are likely externally agile already. Because you have learned to work under pressure since medical school, you might simply call it "being busy." While that may be true, my experience in serving as a coach and facilitator for physicians suggests that additional training on emotional agility is needed. For example, as a new medical director, you attempt to change a protocol that has been a time-proven process. You will most likely be met with great resistance. Staff may tell you "don't fix what isn't broken." To process this resistant response, your inner dialogue needs to be one of understanding that change is often uncomfortable, especially for those who have been doing things a certain way for a long time. This circumstance will require you to use internal agility in your thinking and attitudes. It may require you to use a different approach than just demanding others to comply with your wishes.

As another example, think of the agility that physicians had to develop within themselves to move from paper records to electronic health records (EHRs). Fifteen years ago, I didn't really have a comprehension of the shift to EHRs, but now I have a full understanding of the monster transformation that was required to move medical records online. Many of you would not be accused of being naturally agile while making the EHR transition. There were early adopters for sure, but the majority of physicians were initially resistant. Physicians rely on routines, repetition, and evidenced-based practice, as they should. The shift to EHRs required a whole new set of tools, including psychological agility at the top. Being agile will use a different muscle group than the 'grit' that got you to this point. Grit requires strength and determination while agility relies on quick response and flexibility. Being prepared for the inevitable changing headwinds of healthcare is why I chose to write about agility. Agility is a competency that all physicians can benefit from if they are willing to learn about it and practice it. Confucius stated it this way, "The green reed which bends in the wind is stronger than the mighty oak which breaks in a storm."

Psychologists have coined a term called cognitive rigidity. Cognition refers to your thoughts or thinking. If you are a rigid thinker, you might respond with, "I've never done it that way before" or "I have to do it this way or I will lose it" or "You are wrong, I am right." Perseveration, excessive worry, and rumination are common examples of cognitive rigidity. These thinking 'hiccups' take place when you are under stress, fatigued, or feel unsure. It is your mind's way of protecting itself from unwanted disruptions. Creating a mental fluidity to be open minded is not easy for some people. Family of origin dynamics, personality type, or a controlling boss can all lead people to become fixated on their single-mindedness. If you have this tendency, you may want to consider exploring more fluid ways of thinking.

Being more fluid in your thinking can be as easy as doing things you always do, but simply in a different way. For a season, I was fortunate to be able to work with a spiritual director. In one particular session, she asked me the route I would be driving home from work that day. I explained the best route to take was the expressway and being from the area she was familiar with my directions. What she said next surprised me. "Doug, today when you get on the expressway, I would like for you to get in the right-hand lane and drive the speed limit all the way home." She knew this was a three-lane interstate and the right lane would be the slowest. I laughed and said to myself, "right, no way." It took me a couple drives home to get up the courage to try her technique and when I did, I was stunned at my response. I had a visceral disdain for this exercise. I did not want to do it and in my mind, no one was going to make me. After rehearsing those thoughts for a few minutes, I realized the power of this experience. My thinking was actually making me anxious about completing the task. I had to sit with the experience for several miles until I calmed down. The route was 16 miles on the expressway, which was thankfully enough time to learn the lesson. I will still occasionally slip into the right lane, or brush my teeth with my left hand, or go to the longest wait line at the grocery store, just to remind myself I am not a captive of my own thinking. I am now better at transcending those derailing thoughts and being more content in unwanted circumstances. I challenge you to try it.

Another simple technique is something people with mental fluidity do. They intentionally learn or try something new. One doctor I was working with decided to become more physically active and chose biking. She always wanted to be more active but wasn't athletic and did not find a gym useful. She talked to a few close friends and networked with a couple of colleagues who biked. After research and contemplation, she purchased a starter bike. This launched her into a new hobby. After several weeks, it became almost addicting for her. I had clients who wanted to improve their speaking skills, so they took an improv class. Another colleague's wife decided to paint and found she had a natural talent and really enjoyed it. Regardless of the outcome of trying new things, doing so can always create new neural pathways that can potentially lead to more cognitive flexibility.

Along with thinking flexibility, another path to increased agility is emotional flexibility. By using emotional intelligence assessments in the work environment, I found that some individuals can be highly agile and creative in their thinking, but very rigid emotionally. The reverse can often be true as well. Susan David, a psychologist and author of a wonderful book called *Emotional Agility*, shares her research in finding a behavioral sequence that is reflected in more emotionally agile leaders: *Showing up, stepping out, walking your why*, and *moving on*. The following are some high-level insights to give you a sense of her findings.

SHOWING UP is about facing the reality of your feelings. This sounds simple, but not always easy to do. Many thought leaders use language like, "be brutally honest with yourself" or "cowboy up." David suggests a lighter approach by remaining curious about your feelings, giving yourself permission to experience the full range of emotions.

STEPPING OUT suggests separating yourself from your emotions in order to be reminded that you are separate from and not possessed by your feelings. By stepping out you in essence detach yourself from being controlled by emotions. Taking emotional risks means that you are influenced by emotions, but not consumed by them.

In **WALKING YOUR WHY** David found that people who embrace their 'want to' goals rather than the 'have to' goals seem to stay on purpose and find more grounding in them. This can be a terrific way to establish some healthier boundaries around the dreaded 'shoulds and oughts' that entrap one. By connecting to that deeper want, she maintains you will find more openness to new emotional experiences.

With clarity of your inner goals, you can then **MOVE ON** by aligning your mindset and habits and ensuring they are in service to your "why." Making small, purposeful tweaks seems much more doable than having to perform a complete makeover of your routines. From her perspective, moving on is not moving past, but rather leaning into your new learning.

Mind like water is a powerful reminder of how you can

navigate your career in ways that are less prone to becoming rigid, be more agile both cognitively and emotionally, and avoid unnecessary burnout. Emotional fluidity and cognitive flexibility are irreplaceable resources that can be both elusive and unnatural. You may have a personality that influences your need to avoid change and remain rigid about practices that work for you. Therefore, being intentional and a good student of this concept in action are essential. The good news is that you can *learn* how to be more agile.

CIRQUE DU SOLEIL

"Be aware of wonder. Live a balanced life – learn some and think some and draw and paint and sing and dance and play and work every day some."

~ *Robert Fulgham*

Years ago, I had the opportunity to see Cirque du Soleil, self-described as a contemporary circus. It was an amazing group of athletes and artists who combined their talents into a visual experience that left me saying, "Wow!" The skill set that these entertainers had in common was balancing their bodies in remarkable ways. By bending and stretching they worked together to hold astonishing poses. Yet, in reality, their bodies were always in motion as they gave the illusion of staying still. In a similar way, the bustle and flurry of your own life and career will require that you find ways to keep both in motion rather than trying to balance them equally.

Rather than pursuing balance between work and life, I believe you can aim to create cooperation between them. Do you feel the pressure of, or hear people talk about, achieving work-life balance? I find that striking a healthy balance between two things I love, work and personal life, to be unrealistic. For starters, my work requires much more of my daily time, so 1 am going to lose the so-called 'balance competition' before I even start. I cannot position these two loves as competitors lest I either quit my job or lose my family and friends. Neither choice is acceptable.

In his podcast, Work Life, Adam Grant explains that he landed on the idea of replacing life-work balance with what he calls life-work harmony, meaning he seeks to find a rhythm of cooperation between the two responsibilities. To illustrate, let's compare the tension of work and life to that of being an orchestra conductor. The conductor plays the role of creating harmony by integrating many different instruments into one musical piece. Sometimes all the instruments are playing; at other times certain sections are playing. The musical piece would be less remarkable and unique if everyone played at the same time, all the time. Your life plays out in a similar way. Often, you are called upon to show up and give much to family activities. More times than not, you need to stretch yourself and play strong at work, while other members have to wait and be patient. There may even be times when all eyes are on you, like a first-chair violinist playing a solo while the other orchestra members stand by. Orchestra conductors need to play and highlight certain instruments while keeping the melody going. Likewise, you need to find a way to stay on purpose (melody) while being temporarily focused on one area of life (work) when another (family) must be patient, then vise-versa.

Physicians have told me that their life balance looks more like a lake with rivers flowing from it. The lake is their work life, and the rivers represent their family, friends, and recreation. Everyone gets access to their lake, but physicians don't spend much time on their rivers. One physician I worked with was no longer willing to tolerate the lake metaphor and decided to make a change in his work-life priorities. He decided to shift his work from 70% clinical, 20% research, and 10% education to 90% research and 10% education. This was not an easy choice since he had to resign, move his family to another state, and essentially start over. After starting his new venture, he found himself still working long hours, but in bursts. Additionally, he is home every night to have dinner with his wife and three kids. He intentionally made choices that worked for him and his family. He was able to design a new way of creating

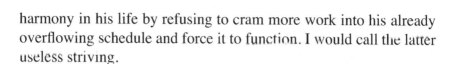

harmony in his life by refusing to cram more work into his already overflowing schedule and force it to function. I would call the latter useless striving.

During my graduate training at the Adler School of Professional Psychology, I learned about the concept of Psychology of Use vs. Psychology of Possession. You may have heard the expression, "I choose to live my life at full choice." This means that I assume ownership of my emotions, thoughts, and behaviors. Adler was convinced that humans *use* their psychological makeup, rather than be *possessed* by it. His studies uncovered that an individual uses his feelings, thinking, and behaviors to help him meet his own goals in life. To be at full choice you must gain mastery of this arrangement. The decision to use your resources versus being controlled by them can lead to completely different outcomes. Surely there are many ways to use your circumstances rather than be a victim of them. For example, a colleague angrily gossips to your staff about the inequity he feels in the surgery rotation implying it is your fault that he doesn't get to perform 'interesting and challenging' surgeries. Upon hearing this, you have a choice. You can use the situation to have a direct conversation with this colleague about his perspective on the surgery rotation and try to find common ground. Or you can become frustrated, defensive, and tell the staff your own version of events, potentially alienating your colleague for good. Which of these approaches will have the best outcome? Remember, you are not the cause of another person's anger or inappropriate conduct. You can only be responsible for your own emotions, thoughts, and behaviors.

Striving to use your resources to the best of your ability is a reminder that there are really only two things you have control of: your *attitude* and your *effort*. That means that any activity beyond your attitude and effort is at risk for being useless. One such attitude might be that you are capable, even though you are not in control. Epictetus, the Greek philosopher said it this way, "Freedom is the only worthy goal in life. It is won by disregarding things that lie beyond our control." If you were to strive to *control* your effort, it would be useless as we all know control is an illusion. As an example, an individual battles an addiction and someone shares with her the 12-step process and serenity prayer: "God, give us grace to accept with serenity the things that cannot be changed, courage to change things which should be changed, and the wisdom to distinguish the one from the other." The primary driver that leads to successful disruption of the power of addiction is the reality and acceptance of what cannot be controlled. That acceptance creates the freedom addicts need to forge their path forward without being constrained by the illusion of control.

Another beneficial way of striving for usefulness is the attitude that you are influenced by emotions, but not consumed by them. T.K. Colman, an educational reformist, encourages his students by saying, "Our feelings are not there to be cast out or conquered. They're there to be engaged and expressed with imagination and intelligence." For example, you have been insulted by a peer at work. It enrages you and is occupying more time and energy than you can afford. You commit to resolve the unwanted emotion by confronting the peer. Recognizing that you are still too angry to confront, you decide to wait and consider your choices. By waiting you deny the emotion the right to drive you to do something you don't really want to do, like alienate a friend or colleague. Gaining that perspective enables you to think of additional options available to you. You are now in a much better position to use your imagination and intelligence in how you choose to move forward. You are becoming more emotionally intelligent. Your *being* is now in the right position to be influencing what it is that you need to be *doing*. Rather than the reverse, whereby doing drives and likely accelerates being agitated.

Martin Luther King Jr. challenged us with another way to be more useful in life by posing this powerful thought, "Life's most persistent and urgent question is, what are you doing for others?" Physicians frequently tell me that they have very little personal space or time to do what they really got into medicine to do, heal patients. I encourage you to come up with your own version of what managing priorities means to you. Do not be passive about this because *what you permit in your life, you promote in your life.* Be at full choice on how you spend your time and who you spend it with. There are no restrictions on being at full choice. For instance, being a full professor has always been a goal of yours. You have pushed yourself, sacrificed much, and set other dreams aside to accomplish this objective. Imagine, as the journey to being a full professor continues, you run into a friend who has already accomplished this milestone. She listens to your concerns and senses your anxiety. With one swift phrase she changes everything for you. She simply asks, "Did you become a physician to earn a title, or to treat disease by caring for patients?" Quite stunned, you leave the conversation thinking about your compulsion toward accomplishment in contrast to the opportunity to serve. Without hesitation you settle back into your first love, caring for patients. The issue of promotion is solved by the urgent question of what am I doing for others today? The reality is if you ask that question first, a promotion is much more likely, than if you don't. The saying "you have to look out for yourself or nobody will" is really just a lie. As Martin Luther King, Jr. suggested, you would be wise to serve others first and the likelihood of your dreams may then be realized. Develop a healthy attitude and apply maximum effort as they are incredible investments that will lead you to more useful striving and thriving in your medical career.

The Cirque du Soleil experience was a magical contemporary circus put on by talented artists and athletes. While you are not on the entertainment stage, you may be in charge of a healthcare floor, wing, or building. Your resiliency quest will likely include the need for acrobatic type maneuvers and a keen insight that maintaining balance is simply understanding that you are in constant motion, need to stay at full choice, and realize that you are only in control of your attitude and effort.

ACTIVATION OF AGILITY

"Agility is the ability to lead effectively under conditions of rapid change and mounting complexity."

~ *Bill Joiner & Stephen Josephs*

Whether you like it or not, life is changing and moving faster than our ability to sometimes enjoy it. There will be ruts and rocks on the trails of life that will require you to be agile. Experts like Joiner and Josephs suggest that agility has become the primary competency needed for consistent success in today's complex, fast-paced work environment. The medical profession qualifies for fast-paced, but inherently demands agility and consequently more agile physician leaders. In my opinion, activating agility is essential to being resilient and to consistently thrive in your role. In their book, *Leadership Agility*, Joiner and Joseph outline four agility capabilities. They are: Context-setting, Stakeholder, Creative, and Self-Leadership. I want to share them with you as they are practical ways to activate agility into your career.

CONTEXT-SETTING AGILITY

Context is decisive, meaning you will not be clear about what you are doing until you have first understood it in its context. Physicians need that perspective on their workplace challenges. Essentially this skill involves you taking a step back, connecting with the wider system and then using the insight to determine the most important initiatives you should focus on. It is like a camera lens zooming out and then back in again. Imagine you are about to work with a patient who has no medical history or lab work of any kind. You only have the symptoms. Certainly, you could move through the diagnostic steps in a methodical manner and eventually make an assessment and plan. However, with more context you can move more swiftly and confidently into a concrete diagnosis and treatment plan.

I had a healthcare executive share a personal story that

illustrates this point well. As finance director, he made a calculation error that ended up costing the company 10 million dollars. After the devastation settled in, he knew he had to come clean. He walked into his boss's office with an envelope in hand. Handing it to his boss, he informed him that due to the enormous and unforgivable mistake, he decided to pre-emptively prepare his resignation letter. His boss sat back in his chair, pondered for a moment, and then swiftly handed the envelope back to him. He simply said, "Son, I just spent 10 million dollars investing in your education. There is no way in hell I am going to let you walk out of here. Now get back to work." This boss clearly understood the context for learning and how to get the most out of his rising star leader. I truly hope that you were given such patience to learn your craft and are now giving those who are entrusted to you the same consideration.

STAKEHOLDER AGILITY

Workplace relationships are essential if you are to be effective in almost any role. I find that healthcare organizations are among the most complex and interdependent entities on the planet. It is understandable that Joiner and Joseph's research would uncover that managing stakeholders is the second of the four essential capabilities. Basically, this agility implies that you know how to enroll your teammates in your assigned initiatives and leverage their abilities to help you achieve them. Medicine, including the clinical and educational aspects, is a huge network of relationships that demands effective skills to navigate it well. You could call this relationship management.

Relationship management is more than just being friendly. It is building bridges with the right people for the right reasons in the right ways. This includes the ability to 'stand in someone else's shoes' in order to really understand that person's needs and align them with your own. It is not a win-lose or lose-win approach where one party is assertive, and the other is accommodating. Instead, you can step out of a win-lose mindset and reach an outcome that supports everyone's agenda and needs, simply put, a win-win mindset.

)(

An obvious way you recognize the need for stakeholder agility is when you move from one hospital or academic institution to another. At your previous organization you knew how to get things done and when not to push too hard. This was learned from years of experience in building bridges with people in hopes of doing a great job. In the new place, none of that is set, so you must start from scratch. One of my clients was lamenting this fact a few months ago and she mentioned how hard it was to get anything done "around here, in this new place." I mentioned that she had a stakeholder challenge and that she would need to build relationships in this new place just as she had in her previous role. She nodded, acknowledging the years it took to build those connections and shrugged her shoulders accepting that she was just at the beginning of a long road. This process cannot be fast tracked. You must do the hard, and often lengthy work of connecting and aligning priorities with your colleagues.

Trust and confidence in teammates go a long way in overcoming any challenges or ambiguity you may endure. They are in fact essential to being resilient. Whether you are new to your organization or a veteran of it, finding trusted colleagues to collaborate with will likely be one of your greatest achievements. The reality is that many medical professionals are not naturally equipped with relationship management skills. The establishment and positive use of trust is by far the most predictive of all human interactions for building relationships. Best-selling author Patrick Lencioni suggests that trust is built by practicing vulnerability-based trust rather than relying on predictability-based trust. He maintains that to earn one's trust by relying on the compulsory keeping of commitments with reliable timelines may often fall short. It is helpful to be reliable and predictable, but some teams or co-worker situations do not have the luxury of time and exposure to build a reservoir of trust. Thus, he recommends that practicing vulnerability with each other will accelerate and sustain a progression of trust in relationships. For example, saying you are sorry or admitting you made a mistake are a few ways Lencioni believes builds sustainable trust between co-workers.

To encourage collaboration and trust I encourage the use of questions. For instance, you may want to start with asking yourself this question: "In what ways are you demonstrating consideration of another's needs, goals, and challenges?" When you begin work initiatives with this question in hand, you are much more likely to create alliances that will indeed support your work initiatives. Let's play out the following scenario as an example. You are asked by your superior to lead a new clinical practice area. This particular area has been a focus of your research and work for the past several years. You are the right choice to lead this clinical initiative. You are very excited and begin to share your excitement with your colleagues, especially the ones you need help from. They are happy for you but frankly they have too much on their own plate to be as excited as you are about this new endeavor. Over the next several weeks you write out protocols and policies based on research which, if followed, will potentially improve this clinical activity immensely. Before you take it to your boss, you want to share your ideas with a few colleagues to get their input. They are less than enthusiastic and, in fact, almost imply that your idea sounds like a lot of extra work. You are getting frustrated and are surprised by their lack of interest in this initiative. You ask yourself, "Why do they not see how important this work is?"

Now you plug in the question I mentioned earlier: "What have I been doing to show my colleagues that I am concerned about their needs, goals, and challenges?" The next time you connect with your co-workers you start the conversation focusing on what they are currently challenged with and trying to accomplish. They will feel heard and valued. What is likely to happen next? They will ask how things are going for you. Now, their curiosity about your work is piqued. You share your experiences with them and before long, you are exploring better options with each other. By practicing this approach, you will begin to move from potentially annoying your colleagues to collaborating with them.

CREATIVE AGILITY

This capability is just what it sounds like - use creativity to transform problems into solutions. There may be a correlation with this agility skill and the saying "never let a perfectly good crisis go to waste." I know physicians must frequently leverage this competency. Recent events in the world have challenged your ability to think quickly on your feet. The pandemic forced everyone to be creatively agile to face the crisis at hand. We all watched the mobile screening centers pop up, emergency facilities were quickly constructed, mask production was handled by adults and children, and innovation was at its best to manufacture ventilators. From daily White House updates to mastering virtual video technology, we all had to rise to the occasion. I am so proud of our healthcare workforce for the way they responded to the unexpected and unwanted intrusion of COVID-19. I hope we never need to be creative in this reactive way again. A heartwarming story that demonstrated creativity during the quarantine era can be found in the RV for MD's campaign. A Facebook group was formed that allows RV owners to post their travel trailer, fifth wheel, pop ups, and motorhomes for healthcare workers to use for self-quarantine purposes and stay close to their families. The group, started by a Texas mother of three seeking an RV for her husband, an emergency room physician, quickly grew due to the demand for others in the same situation. This group became a reliable source for physicians with extreme self-distancing needs.

The unlimited tricky situations that physicians routinely face require creative agility. Physicians are trained to solve problems. As challenges increase in complexity, such as COVID-19, it is imperative that physicians become more aware of ways to be creatively agile. One idea is to practice no-box thinking. You have heard the expression "be an out of the box thinker" to help encourage thinking in non-traditional ways. A way to accelerate that creativity is to remove the "box" so to speak and start from a clean slate. Strive to remove all previously used assumptions and invent a new path forward. You can also start that journey by utilizing the activation protocols at the end of this trailhead.

SELF-LEADERSHIP AGILITY

This fourth agility capability is self-explanatory. It requires that you leverage your experience and education into being a continuous learner. Past thought leaders promoted the idea of constantly growing and learning.

- *"Learning never exhausts the mind"*
  ~ *Leonardo da Vinci*

- *"Man's mind, once stretched by a new idea, never regains its original dimensions"*
  ~ *Oliver Wendell Holmes*

- *"The doer alone learned"*
  ~ *Friedrich Nietzsche*

- *"I don't think much of a man who is not wiser today than he was yesterday"*
  ~ *Abraham Lincoln*

One of the primary barriers to achieve self-leadership agility is being unwilling to be a learning physician. Physicians follow protocols and procedures until they discover they don't work. Then they are challenged. For some, it takes too much time and effort to grow and develop, so they default to doing what has always worked. As it is often said, we are eloquently designed to get the results we are getting. So, if you want to get a better result, you are going to have to change and learn something new.

Early in my consulting career I was coaching a healthcare finance specialist who was overqualified for his job. He was an accountant and attorney but didn't enjoy practicing law. He landed a finance job in a provider-based firm and enjoyed the security. His boss announced that he would be retiring in the next 18 months. During a coaching session, my client told me he wanted his boss's job. However, he was convinced the executive team didn't like him; therefore, he did not believe he would be considered for the promotion. I asked him what they wanted from him. He responded, "They want me to wear a tie and act like them, and I'll be damned if I am going to do that." I asked him if he wanted the promotion enough to play along with me and try something. Using a vintage coaching technique, I asked him if he would be willing to act 'as if' he already had the position. He agreed to try but admitted that it meant he would have to wear a tie, so he was very pessimistic. Nevertheless, he wore a tie every day for a week and role-played as if he were in his boss's role. Much to his surprise, one positive response after another started rolling in. Then, one thing led to another and within nine months he was awarded the promotion. In this case, wearing a tie allowed him to move to an office with a door and a 40% increase in salary. Replacing his old pattern of dressing how he wanted to for the 'tie' approach, allowed my client the opportunity to transform his self-image so he could have the security of a steady job and the reward of executive salary. Sometimes changing something as simple as your resistance to work attire to embracing the 'act as if' technique can eventually lead to a new pattern of behavior.

The skill of being agile in your self-leadership reminds you to take the opportunity and time to reflect and learn. As you prepare to face the challenges of each day, prepare yourself for the journey you will be on. Unfortunately, few physician leaders take the time to self-reflect. Don't be one of those. If you embrace your own development, it will have a significant impact on your performance and potential for greater things. In addition, when you feel you are living up to your image of the leader you want to be, or making progress towards this, your confidence and productivity increases.

Activation of agility implies action. For physicians to remain effective and relevant, they must handle multiple curve balls thrown their way. Engaging in your work without expecting ruts and rocks is unrealistic. Whether it is the digital revolution or ever-changing healthcare demands, a ridiculous dress code change or a radical unwanted pandemic, they all require a constant state of innovation and learning.

CHANGE AGILITY HABITS

"And once you understand that habits can change, you have the freedom and the responsibility to remake them."

~ *Charles Duhigg*

Agility is essentially change in motion. If you want to become more resilient you will have to modify what you have been doing that hasn't been working well for you. It all boils down to making changes in your current thoughts, emotions and behaviors. To be sure, the drive to change is based on your source of motivation. Conventional wisdom holds that you can motivate someone to change by showering them with facts, making them read books, invoking fear of punishment, or otherwise forcing your superiority onto them. If you ask a group of your physician peers (and I have) how they feel about being forced to change, the response is some variation of, "tell me why we need to change" or "prove to me what is not working about the way we are doing it now." They flat out reject this conventional wisdom and rely on their own instincts and logic. So, if this conventional wisdom is not true for them, as well as many other people groups, then why do bosses, parents, or organizations focus on change in this way? The reality is that they all keep doing what they have always done, especially organizations, because change is hard! How you view change needs to be reconsidered.

Since change is inevitable, it might be helpful to develop habits for change in order to be prepared when the need to change shows up on your doorstep. If you want to thrive instead of struggle, be forward focused rather than reactive, change because you choose to and not because you have to, or embrace self-responsibility over being a victim then you will want to incorporate the following evidenced based habits from Alan Deutschman's exceptional book, *Change or Die*. It is about how people and organizations can embrace change and even benefit from it. He shares several real-life cases of leaders from all walks of life, such as medical professionals, sociologists, corporate executives and entrepreneurs, where conventional wisdom was entirely counter-productive. In each case, leaders defied traditional methods and blazed a new trail, successfully inducing dramatic and life-altering change in their patients, career criminals, workers, and companies. Deutschman researched the stories of these leaders and identified thematic habits each leader used to induce meaningful, personal change in others and themselves. These habits are Relate, Repeat, and Reframe.

To illustrate these ideas, let's imagine you want to change the way you work with your boss. You tend to be hesitant and a bit fearful to engage with him and want to change that mindset to become more confident in your interactions. It's a daunting feat, but one well worth pursuing. Even though you want to change, you don't have any idea where to start. It may be possible for you to do this without any outside counsel. However, since you wouldn't change a tricky medical treatment without seeking feedback, the same goes for inducing meaningful change in your life. It's always easier and more effective to do it with others rather than go it alone. And on that note, let's begin with the first habit.

HABIT #1: RELATE

"You form a new emotional relationship with a person or community that inspires and sustains hope."

Of course, lasting change requires the belief that you actually *can* change. Not just belief in yourself, though that is certainly an essential component, but the belief in you from others as well. Others may include a mentor or community of some kind that has mastered the thing you want to change about yourself. Finding this person or community is not always easy, but well worth the effort. Sometimes they are new and sometimes they are already a part of your life. You also need to believe that your chosen mentor or community has the knowledge and skills necessary to teach you what you need to learn. In your situation, you need to find someone who is confidently working well with his or her boss. The individual does not have to be a physician, but that may be helpful. Once you find them, invite them to provide support for you and your goal. Deutschman points out that a mentor relationship requires an *emotional* component. It is not a mere transactional relationship. Just as your patients want a relationship with you, their healer, you want someone who will invest and believe you are able to make strides toward becoming bold and confident. Like any goal worth pursuing, making a substantial change requires accountability, patience, and time, which leads to the next key to change.

HABIT #2: REPEAT

"The new relationship helps you learn, practice, and master the new habits and skills that you'll need."

Tony Robbins, a well-known motivational speaker and author, once said that "repetition is the mother of all skill." Once you've enrolled a mentor and made an emotional connection, the mentor will teach you everything they can about your desired area of change and how to implement the lessons in your own life because they have walked that road. It is up to you to put these lessons into action, though. Change, like any skill, requires regular practice of it in your life in order for it to stick; simply *knowing* what you need to do is not enough in the long run. This habit is all about repetition. Practice makes perfect, as the saying goes. Preparing and rehearsing are proven behaviors to create sustainable change. Samuel Johnson, an English writer and poet, once said, "The chains of habit are too weak to be felt until they are too strong to be broken." Habits are those behaviors that we hardwire into our operating system. Everyone has habits, but few are so keenly aware of them that they can leverage these patterns into intentional living. Repetition is an essential and valuable skill. Malcolm Gladwell suggested in his book *Outliers* that we need 10,000 hours of practice before something becomes a strength. Think back to anything you are good at and how many reps you did to be competent at it. This is why connecting with others is so imperative. Your mentor and community are there to help you, to pick you up when you are down, to remind you that you *can* do this and that they believe you will succeed. They are your change coach, your support team, your companions on the path to a courageous and confident working relationship with your boss. And when you have achieved a healthy perspective, you find assurance in your newly developed abilities.

HABIT #3: REFRAME

"The new relationship helps you learn new ways of thinking about your situation and your life."

At some point your paradigm will have to shift. What and how you thought, felt, and behaved about your personal desire to change will eventually have to change. Personal change is so inherently transformational that it's impossible to look at the world the same way ever again. Deutschman says it best, "Ultimately, you look at the world in a way that would have been so foreign to you that it wouldn't have made any sense to you before you changed." If you are still looking at the world, or in this case approaching your boss, the same way before you started the change, you aren't finished yet. My encouragement is that you will need to practice a new mantra or reshape a belief system about the hesitation you have in approaching your boss. Prior to connecting with your mentor and practicing assertiveness you believed you could not approach your boss and be bold and articulate. Now you have a newfound perspective that you can face him with confidence. If you consistently connect with your mentor and community and actively reinforce the ideas and practical steps they share with you to lessen your fear and increase your confidence, a new mindset will emerge and become the new normal for how you interact with your boss.

Deustchman's three Rs are fantastic methods to induce meaningful, personal change. However, you must remember that there is one irrefutably essential ingredient to this process: an *active, willing participant*. In other words, YOU! Meaningful, personal change is just that: personal. It's not passive. It's not something that happens *to* you. It happens *because* of you. It happens as a result of your desire to change, belief that you will change, and perseverance in making the change a reality. At the end of the day, change happens because *you* make it happen.

HIGHLIGHTS OF THE AGILITY TRAILHEAD

MIND LIKE WATER:
Mind like water is a powerful reminder of how you can navigate your career in ways that are less prone to becoming rigid, more agile both cognitively and emotionally, and avoid unnecessary burnout. Emotional fluidity and cognitive flexibility are irreplaceable resources that can be both elusive and unnatural.

CIRQUE DU SOLEIL:
Rather than pursuing balance between work and life, I believe you can aim to create cooperation between them....Your resiliency quest will likely include the need for acrobatic type maneuvers and a keen insight that maintaining balance is simply understanding that you are in constant motion, need to stay at full choice, and realize that you are only in control of your attitude and effort.

ACTIVATION OF AGILITY:
Activation of agility implies action. For physicians to remain effective and relevant, they must handle multiple curve balls thrown their way. Engaging in your work without expecting ruts and rocks is unrealistic. Whether it is the digital revolution or ever-changing healthcare demands, a ridiculous dress code change or a radical unwanted pandemic, they all require a constant state of innovation and learning.

CHANGE AGILITY HABITS:
To induce meaningful, personal change....you must remember that there is one irrefutably essential ingredient to this process: an *active, willing participant*. In other words, YOU! Meaningful, personal change is just that: personal. It's not passive. It's not something that happens *to* you. It happens *because* of you. It happens as a result of your desire to change, belief that you will change, and perseverance in making the change a reality.

AGILITY ACTIVATION

Resilient physician leaders are mentally and emotionally agile.
- You understand the difference between IQ and EQ.
- You develop "psychological muscle" from the practice of emotional intelligence.
- Being agile enough to bend but not break is the key.

AGILITY PROTOCOL

PROFESSIONAL ASSISTED ACTION

Consider taking a formal 360 assessment. Contact our Resiliency Quest network administrator for a referral to complete one of these assessments at TheResiliencyQuest@gmail.com.

- **Leadership Agility 360:**
  https://assessleadershipagility.com/
- **EQ 360:**
  https://storefront.mhs.com/collections/eq-360

SELF-DIRECTED ACTION

1. ***Mental Agility:*** Black and White thinking
   - Blinkist: Read the summary on Thinking Fast and Slow.
   - Work Life Podcast with Adam Grant. Listen to: Relationships at Work with Esther Perel.

2. ***Emotional Agility:*** Read the book *Emotional Agility* by Susan David
   - Take the free online assessment in the book. https://www.susandavid.com/ea-quiz

3. *Stretch yourself:* You can teach an old dog new tricks
   - Take up a new hobby like playing an instrument or painting.
   - Volunteer for an unfamiliar cause and get involved with learning how to help them.
   - Offer to lead a new initiative at work that you know nothing about.

COLLATERAL BEAUTY

"The most beautiful people I've known are those who have known trials, have known struggles, have known loss, and have found their way out of the depths."

~ *Elizabeth Kübler-Ross*

Louise likes to observe more than talk. In a group she will generally stay on the perimeter reading people's body language and listening intently to their words. When she speaks it is with a quick wit, plain truth, and an accent that somehow combines New York City and North Carolina. As Louise is about to deliver the truth, she will often preface it with "I got nothin' left to lose."

After disasters such as tornadoes or hurricanes, you may hear people say that they lost everything, but I imagine few have actually lost to the extent that Louise has. On the night of March 6, 2012 her husband Duane and daughters Bella (6) and Natalia (4) perished in a fire that began suddenly and quickly engulfed their entire home. "When I went to sleep, I was a wife and a mother. I had a beautiful family and home, and all that goes with it. Hours later it was all gone. Everything was gone."

Although this was her most devastating blow, it wasn't the first. Life had not been easy from the start. She lived in various parts of New York where her father worked days as a trash collector and nights as the superintendent of the building. It was not a loving home filled with hugs, kisses and kind words. The neighborhoods weren't great. There was crime, bullying and isolation. Louise focused on caring for those around her and being 'a good kid', so as to not add to the family's difficulties.

Her father died when she was 15 leaving her to care for her

mother who was an abusive alcoholic. Louise and her mom moved to Austin, Texas to start new with the hopes of having more stability. She worked two jobs to support them while still going to school, sometimes falling asleep in class. She graduated high school and earned an ROTC scholarship to help with college. But her home obligations kept her from finishing, and she moved back to care for her mom. Why, you might ask? "It's all I knew. I didn't know what love or a good life looked like. This was all I knew and so I lived the life I had."

But a few years later that all changed on a trip to visit her brother stationed at an Army base in Italy. There she met a "tough, bad ass soldier with a soft, needy side." They married soon after and moved to a beautiful old home in North Carolina where Duane began the process of training for Army Special Forces. Bella and Natalia joined them over the next few years.

While Duane deployed often and to dangerous places, life was somewhat idyllic. Louise had vowed that her daughters would only know love and a good life. She dedicated herself to fulfilling that promise every day. She had the home, love, and life that she never knew possible. And then, in a matter of minutes, it was gone. After the tragedy, it took two years before she could even say the girls' names out loud, and more before the shock of what happened slowly dissipated. She bounced around staying with friends, or other Army families, and even committed herself to psychiatric care on and off. She drank and medicated heavily during that period – anything that would block the new reality of her life. She says she never really considered suicide, but each night she would wash down a handful of pills with a couple of bottles of wine to numb the pain hoping she didn't wake up. But she always did.

After the fire, honors and accolades were heaped upon Duane, who had already been highly decorated for action and valor prior to the fire. During these ceremonies, rarely were the girls recognized beyond a general mention. Louise attended all of these ceremonies with her mind numb, a smile plastered on her face, and growing despair in her heart. Her girls had also lived, loved and been loved. They deserved to be known and remembered. It was this stark realization that finally propelled her out of her shock and despair. Bella and Natalia, like many little girls, had loved to twirl and dance. When their Daddy was gone to far away places, they attended dance lessons and recitals, transmitting videos of their plies and pirouettes to a soft-hearted soldier who would watch and smile. Louise began to entertain the idea of keeping their memory alive through dance, and soon the Dancing Angels Foundation was created.

Today Louise lives quietly in a home that she designed and built, on a large parcel of quiet North Carolina countryside. She spends her days working on the foundation, meeting with and talking to young dancers, and providing scholarships for their continued education. She also speaks and works with others who are grieving. And while she firmly believes that the magnitude of her grief and loss should never outweigh anyone else's, she has little patience for those who want to wallow in despair or depression. It's not beyond her to listen patiently for hours and then with a no-nonsense edge in her voice simply say "man you need to get your act together, this is the only life you have, and you damn well better start living it. Tomorrow isn't promised."

I trust you understand and appreciate why I shared this story. Louise has endured things that are unimaginable, yet she has become a heroic role model for hundreds of military families, finds time to care for others, routinely enjoys humor in practical things, and continues to be engaged in her life. Every conversation I have with her is both encouraging and inspiring. When I asked if I could share her story with all of you, she humbly said that she would trust me to know if it would be helpful to my readers. She then asked me if I'd ever seen the movie *Collateral Beauty*, which encourages involvement in selfless acts of kindness after experiencing tragedy. Louise went on to explain that the movie reflects how she now feels about her life. What a remarkable reframe of such a painful and unimaginable experience.

You may be asking, "What does her story have to do with me?" First, remember you are working with patients who may be doing heroic things every day as part of the healing journey that you are leading them into. Second, stories inspire us to uncover collateral beauty all around us. A concept known as vicarious resilience maintains that those who witness resilience in others often experience personal growth and resilience in their own lives. A physician client of mine says it well: "For us not to derive meaning from the resilience of our patients is a real missed opportunity." And third, notice that Louise is on a life-long resiliency quest, not a one-off hike. I hope that by reading her heartbreaking, yet inspiring story you too will be open to notice that in all of the pain, frustration, and challenges you currently have or may endure in your career, there is beauty.

)(

CLOSING COMMENTS

As the cover of this book illustrates, resiliency can be both challenging and adventurous. The journey or quest is not going to be a walk in the park, but more like a hike up the mountain. Nothing is guaranteed nor easy. I hope that my stories and the key themes of this book have demonstrated the unique parallel between hiking in nature and resiliency in your life and workplace. Trailheads are symbolic markers that show you are on the path toward something. Your trailheads may be different than mine, but both serve to guide and point us in the right direction. Many milestones and peak experiences will keep you faithful to your journey if you choose to stop and celebrate them.

Having trained to become a physician, you and your contribution are an invaluable resource to your coworkers and the healthcare field. I encourage you to work boldly and engage fully in the struggle to improve our healthcare system. Be the change you want to see in the system. Open yourself up to new experiences and don't be confined by fear and the need to appear strong or in control. If you are willing to be even five percent more vulnerable with your coworkers, friends and family, I predict you will experience a resilient life similar to what Louise does now, as a living example of collateral beauty.

May your quest for resiliency be one of intentional curiosity that leads you to experience a new awareness of self, unique connections, settled boundaries, positive emotional agility, and a revived sense of purpose.

Stay the course and enjoy the journey.

It is worth it.

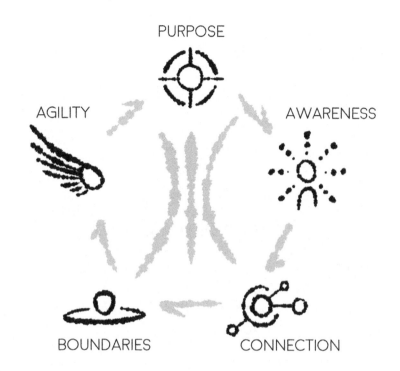

PURPOSE	Leads to values-based motivation.
AWARENESS	Leads to improving your power to choose.
CONNECTION	Leads to healthier relationships.
BOUNDARIES	Lead to more freedom to be yourself.
AGILITY	Leads to expanded openness to change.

END NOTES

THE RESILIENCY QUEST:

American Psychological Association. The road to resilience. Washington, DC: American Psychological Association; 2014.

Goleman, D. (1995). Emotional intelligence. New York: Bantam Books.

PURPOSE TRAILHEAD

SIMON BIRCH:

Steven-Johnson, M. (Director). (1998). *Simon Birch*. [Film]. Hollywood Pictures, Caravan Pictures.

Sinek, S. (2011). *Start with why: How great leaders inspire everyone to take action*. Portfolio.

SECRETS OF THE SEQUOIA:

Cahill, A. (2000). *Nature's masterpiece: Giant sequoia*. Pacific Horticulture Society. *https://www.pacifichorticulture.org/articles/natures-masterpiece-giant-sequoia/*

DON'T BE DECEIVED:

Ruben, G. (2015). The happiness project: Or, why I spent a year trying to sing in the morning, clean my closets, fight right, read Aristotle, and generally have more fun. Harper Paperbacks.

Gilbert, D. (2007). *Stumbling into happiness*. Vintage.

Ruffing, J. (1995). Resisting the demon of busyness. *Spiritual Life: A quarterly of contemplative spirituality. (41)2.*

SELF-AWARENESS TRAILHEAD

WINDOWPANES:

Luft, J. (1969). *Of human interaction: The Johari model.* Mayfield Publishers

Fiuza, M. (2018). *Behind the Johari Window. Professional Development Blog, Institute of Coaching, Mclean, Affiliate of Harvard Medical School*, August 28

Cashman, K. (2017). *Leadership from the inside out: Becoming a leader for life.* Berrett-Koehler Publishers, 3rd Edition.

INNER TRUTH:

Parker Palmer. *Let Your Life Speak*, Jossey-Bass 1999

Smith, H. (2000). *What matters most,* Simon Schuster, New York, NY.

Shirkani, J. (2013). Ego vs. EQ: How top leaders beat 8 ego traps with emotional intelligence. Routledge.

PRE-SCRIPT-IONS:

Brooks, R. & Goldstein, S. (2004). *The Power of Resilience.* McGraw Hill Books.

Sotile, W., Sotile, M. (2002). *The resilient physician.* American Medical Association.

CONNECTION TRAILHEAD

THE THREE WISE MONKEYS:

Bishop, O. (2007, February, 8). *Sawubono*. (Video). YouTube Video. https://www.youtube.com/watch?v=2IjUkVZRPK8

Brown, B. (2010). *The gifts of imperfections*. Hazelden Publishing.

Salovey, Peter, Marc A Brackett, and John D Mayer. (2004). Emotional Intelligence. Port Chester, N.Y.: Dude Pub., 2004. Print.

Kimsey-House, K., Kimsey-House, H., Sandahl, P., Whitworth, L. (2011). *Co-active coaching*. Nicholas Brealey Publications.

MULLIGAN PLEASE:

Powers, C. (2011). *Did You Know: Where did the term 'mulligan' originate?* Golf Digest.com

Georgi Tushkan, G. (1944). *The hunter of the pamirs: A novel of adventure in soviet central asia*. Hutchison Publishers.

Goleman, Daniel. (2004). What makes a leader? Harvard Business Review. January

LAW OF WILSON:

Dutton, J.E. and Heaphy, E.D. (2003). The power of high-quality connections, in *positive organizational scholarship*. Berrett-Koehler.

Zemeckis, R. (Director). (2000). *Cast Away*. [Film]. Twentieth Century Fox, Dream Works Pictures.

Glasser, J. (2016). *Conversational intelligence: How great leaders build trust and get extraordinary results*. Routledge.

THE COURAGE TO BE IMPERFECT:

Adler, A. (1963). *Understanding human nature*. Premier.

Adler, A. (1998). *What life should mean to you*. Hazelton.

Brown, B. (2018). *Dare to lead*. Random House.

Boyatsis, R. McKee, A. (2005). Resonate leadership. Harvard Business School Press.

BOUNDARIES TRAILHEAD

BOULDER AND THE BACKPACK:

Cloud, H., Townsend, J. (1992). *When to say yes, how to say no to take control of your life*. Zondervan.

Cloud, H. (2013). Boundaries for leaders: Results, relationships, and being ridiculously in charge. Harper Business.

TATTOOS, ACCENTS, AND ATTIRE:

Banaji, M., Greenwald, A. (2016). *Blindspot: Hidden biases of good people*. Bantam

Cloud, H. (2016). *The Power of the other: The startling effect other people have on you, from the boardroom to the bedroom and beyond-and what to do about it*. Harper Business.

PLAYING FULL OUT:

Huffington, A. (2014). *Thrive: The third metric to redefining success and creating a life of well-being, wisdom, and wonder.* Harmony.

Williamson, M. (1996). *A return to love: Reflections on the principles of "a course in miracles".* HarperOne

RIVERBANKS:

Gibson, M. (Director). (2016). *Hacksaw Ridge* [film]. Summit Entertainment.

Lipsenthal, L. (2007). *Finding balance in a medical life.* Lee Lipsenthal, MD.

AGILITY TRAILHEAD

MIND LIKE WATER:

Allen, D. (2001). *Getting things done. The art of stress-free productivity.* Viking.

Coplin, J. (2016, August, 1). *Cognitive Rigidity; The 8-ball from hell.* Psychology Today.

David, S. (2016). Emotional Agility: Get unstuck, embrace change, and thrive in work and life. Avery.

CIRQUE DU SOLEIL:

Grant, A. (2019). *Work Life*. Podcast with Adam Grant

Ansbacher, H.L., Ansbacher, R.R. (1964). *The individual psychology of Alfred Adler: A systematic presentation in selections from his writings*. Harper Perennial.

Caruso, D. Salovey, P., (2004). The Emotionally Intelligent Manager: How to develop and use the four key emotional skills of leadership. Jossey-Bass.

ACTIVATION OF AGILITY:

Joiner, W. Josephs, S. (2006). *Leadership agility: Five levels of mastery for anticipating and initiating change*. Jossey-Bass.

Lencioni, P. (2002). *The five dysfunctions of a team: A leadership fable*. Jossey-Bass

CHANGE AGILITY HABITS:

Deutschman, A. (2007). *Change or die*. Harper Business.

Duhigg, C. (2014). *The power of a habit*: Why we do what we do in life and business. Random House
Collateral Beauty:

Frankel, D. (Director). (2016). *Collateral Beauty*. [Film]. New Line Cinema, Village Roadshow Pictures.

ABOUT THE AUTHOR

Doug has been a clinical psychologist for over 30 years and has invested the past 20 years of his career as a Master Coach facilitating change in leaders and organizations. He is frequently invited to work with leadership teams in building more cohesion and leveraging greater impact. He often consults on leadership development, conflict mediation, and culture transformation as well as speaking and facilitating at leadership retreats.

When not working with humans, you can find Doug consulting with the mountains of Colorado as he is an avid hiker. Doug and his wife Jana live in the Chicagoland area. They enjoy traveling, taking long walks, and spending time with their two adult children.

For more information on his consulting services, you can reach Doug at:

doug@dlmpathways.com
DLMPathways.com
linkedin.com/in/dougmckinley

Made in the USA
Coppell, TX
20 October 2021